2nd Edition

Examining Food & Nutrition

For GCSE

Jenny Ridgwell

www.heinemann.co.uk
✓ Free online support
✓ Useful weblinks
✓ 24 hour online ordering

0845 630 22 22

Heinemann

Part of Pearson

Heinemann is an imprint of Pearson Education Limited,
a company incorporated in England and Wales, having its
registered office at Edinburgh Gate, Harlow, Essex, CM20 2JE.
Registered company number: 872828

www.heinemann.co.uk

Heinemann is a registered trademark of Pearson Education
Limited

Text © Pearson Education Limited 2009

First published 2009

12 11 10 09
10 9 8 7 6 5 4 3

British Library Cataloguing in Publication Data
A catalogue record for this book is available from the
British Library

ISBN 978 0 435 420 71 0

Edited by Sarah Christopher
Typeset by Tek-Art
Original illustrations © Pearson Education Limited
Cover photo © Masterfile
Printed in China (CTPS/03)

Websites
There are links to relevant websites in this book. In order to
ensure that the links are up to date, that the links work, and
that the sites are not inadvertently linked to sites that could
be considered offensive, we have made the links available on
the Heinemann website at www.heinemann.co.uk/hotlinks.
When you access the site, the express code is 0710P.

CONTENTS

Acknowledgements vi
Introduction vii

Chapter 1: Nutrition and health 2

Current dietary guidelines 2
5 A DAY campaign 4
The eatwell plate 1 6
The eatwell plate 2 8
Dietary reference values 1 10
Dietary reference values 2 12
Energy from food 1 14
Energy from food 2 16
Excess weight and obesity 1 18
Excess weight and obesity 2 20
Diet and health 1 22
Diet and health 2 24
Digestion 26
Macronutrients: Protein 28
Macronutrients: Fats 1 30
Macronutrients: Fats 2 32
Macronutrients: Carbohydrates 34
Macronutrients: Starches 36
Macronutrients: Sugars 38
Dietary fibre 40
Micronutrients: Vitamins 1 42
Micronutrients: Vitamins 2 44
Micronutrients: Minerals 1 46
Micronutrients: Minerals 2 48
Salt and sodium 50
Water and alcohol 52
Exam café 54

Contents

Chapter 2: People and food needs   **56**

Dietary needs: Age differences and pregnancy   56
Dietary needs: Babies   58
Dietary needs: Toddlers and young children 1   60
Dietary needs: Toddlers and young children 2   62
Dietary needs: Teenagers   64
Dietary needs: Adults   66
Food for sport and exercise   68
Vegetarians 1   70
Vegetarians 2   72
Food intolerance 1   74
Food intolerance 2   76
School meals   78
Religion and food choices   80
Exam café   82

Chapter 3: Food and cooking   **84**

Meat and poultry   84
Fish and seafood   86
Eggs   88
Milk, cheese and yogurt   90
New protein: Quorn™ and novel foods   92
Fruit and vegetables   94
Beans and pulses, nuts and seeds   96
Potatoes   98
Cereals   100
Bread   102
Additives   104
Convenience food   106
Cooking methods 1   108
Cooking methods 2   110
Effect of heat on food   112
Properties and functions of ingredients   114
Properties and functions: Flour   116
Properties and functions: Sugar   118
Properties and functions: Fats   120
Raising agents   122
Changes that take place in cooking   124
Acids and alkalis in cooking   126
Cooking equipment   128
Exam café   130

Chapter 4: Food hygiene and safety — 132

Food spoilage 1   132
Food spoilage 2   134
Food hygiene and safety   136
Food poisoning 1   138
Food poisoning 2   140
Exam café   142

Chapter 5: Food preservation and storage — 144

Refrigerators and freezers   144
Preservation 1   146
Preservation 2   148
Food labelling 1   150
Food labelling 2   152
Food packaging   154
Recycling food packaging   156
Exam café   158

Chapter 6: Factors affecting consumer choice — 160

Advertising and marketing research   160
Household and shopping trends   162
Ethical shopping   164
Food production and sustainability   166
Ethical food labels   168
Cost of food   170
Buying goods and consumer help   172
Food in the news   174
Exam café   176

Preparing for assessment — 178

Making food to eat, cooking skills   178
Tasting and testing 1   180
Tasting and testing 2   182
Assessment   184
Research   186
Planning a practical solution to the task   188
Task analysis   190
ICT for food work   192

Food Acts   194
Glossary   196
Index   199

Acknowledgements

Every effort has been made to contact copyright holders of material reproduced in this book. Any omissions will be rectified in subsequent printings if notice is given to the publishers.

Websites of the following organisations can be found by going to www.heinemann.co.uk/hotlinks and entering the express code 0710P.

Pages 3, 6, 8, 95: © Crown copyright material is reproduced with the permission of the Controller of HMSO and Queen's Print for Scotland.
Page 5: 5 A DAY images used with permission of NSF-CMi.
Page 10: screenshot used with permission of the British Nutrition Foundation.
Page 11: spinach and ricotta pizza recipe reproduced by kind permission of Sainsbury's Supermarkets Ltd.
Page 52: 'Water is Cool in School' poster used with permission of ERIC.
Page 52: alcohol guidelines reproduced with permission of the Department of Health.
Page 72: quote used with permission of the Vegan Society.
Pages 71, 168: logo used with permission of the Vegetarian Society.
Pages 76, 168: symbol used with permission of Coeliac UK.
Pages 85, 168: logo used with permission of the RSPCA.
Pages 85, 168: logo used with permission of Assured Food Standards (AFS).
Page 89: Lion Quality mark used with permission of the British Egg Information Service.
Page 160: logo used with permission of Ofcom.
Pages 165, 168: logo used with permission of Carbon Footprint Ltd.
Pages 165, 168: logo used with permission of the Fairtrade Foundation.
Pages 166, 168: logo used with permission of Organic Farmers & Growers.
Pages 166, 168: logo used with permission of the Soil Association.
Page 170: screenshot used with permission of mySupermarket.co.uk, 'the UK's grocery comparison website'.
Page 173: screenshot used with permission of Which?

Photo acknowledgements
© Alamy: page 18 (Dave Jepson), page 31 (Ashley Cooper), page 67 (David Taylor), page 73 (ShaunFinch), page 80 (Chloe Johnson), page 91 (mediablitzimages (uk) Limited), page 92 (Geoffrey Kidd), page 128 (UrbanZone), page 132 (Tony Cunningham), page 135 (Scott Tilley), page 118 (sciencephotos), page 118 (mediablitzimages (uk) Limited), page 162 (Les Gibbon), page 163 (Scott Hortop Images), page 164 (Alex Segre), page 166 (Sam Toren), page 171 (Detail Nottingham), page 173 (Macana).
© Alpro UK: page 46.
© Corbis: page 25 (Bettmann), page 49 (Medical Objects), page 69 (Michael Cole).
© Dorset Cereals: page 41.
© Fotolia.com: page 102 (mark huls).
© Fruisana: page 119.
© iStockphoto: page 91 (Linda & Colin McKie), page 100 (Thammarat Kaosombat), page 100 (LyaC).
© Just Kosher: page 80.
© Pearson Education: page 96 (Rob Judges), page 136 (Jules Selmes).
© PhotoDisc: page 98 (Photolink. S. Meltzer), page 100.
© Photos.com. Jupiterimages: page 97.
© Science Photo Library: page 132 (NIBSC), page 132 (John Durham).
© Shutterstock: page 16 (Maxim Slugin), page 22 (Piotr Rzeszutek), page 23 (Douglas Freer), page 32 (marcstock), page 110 (Picsfive), page 111 (trailexplorers), page 126 (Tihis).
© Silverspoon: page 118.
© Tate & Lyle: page 118.

Introduction

The specification for Home Economics focuses on food and nutrition issues in relation to nutrition, diet and health throughout life, factors affecting consumer choice, the nutritional, physical, chemical and sensory properties of foods in storage, preparation and cooking, food hygiene, safety and techniques and skills used in food storage, preparation and cooking.

GCSE specifications in Home Economics require students to plan and carry out investigations and tasks in which they analyse issues and problems, identify, gather and record relevant information and evidence, then analyse and evaluate evidence and make reasoned judgements and present conclusions.

Students will develop knowledge and understanding of human needs within a diverse society and relevant technological and scientific developments.

GCSE specifications in Home Economics must enable learners to:

- actively engage in the processes of Home Economics to develop as effective and independent learners.
- develop their knowledge and understanding of human needs within a diverse society
- develop their knowledge and understanding of relevant technological and scientific developments
- develop a critical and analytical approach to decision-making and problem-solving in relation to the specified context
- examine issues that affect the quality of human life including an appreciation of diversity
- evaluate choices and decisions to develop as informed and discerning consumers.

How to use this book

The book is organised into sections which relate to the Home Economics GCSE specification content. The sections in the book are:

- Nutrition and health
- People and food needs
- Food and cooking
- Food hygiene and safety
- Food preservation and storage
- Consumer choice.

Each section progresses through the specifications and aims to cover the contents of all the exam boards. New and up-to-date food issues have been included, since these are important for future food studies.

Home economics and food education are constantly changing as new nutritional guidelines and food laws are introduced. Manufacturers are introducing new products in line with healthy eating guidelines, and new ingredients are being created. This book reflects the modern trends in eating habits and popular foods.

Useful websites are provided for further work, and where possible, there are investigations which can involve practical tasks. An exam café can be found at the end of sections to give tips and help with revision.

Current dietary guidelines

A diet is made up of all the foods and drinks that you eat. We need to eat food for growth, repair, energy, normal body functioning, warmth and good health.

The Government has issued several guidelines to help us eat a healthy diet (see opposite).

Guidelines include:

- 8 tips for eating well
- 5 A DAY
- the eatwell plate
- dietary reference values.

The Licence to Cook programme helps students to learn to cook and understand the principles of food hygiene, diet and nutrition, and consumer issues.

WEBSITES

- Food Standards Agency
- British Nutrition Foundation
- Licence to Cook

What is a healthy diet?

Two important things are:

- to eat the right amount of food for how active you are
- to eat a range of foods to make sure you're getting a balanced diet.

There are no unhealthy foods, but if we eat too much of some types of food, such as sweets and crisps, then our diet will be unhealthy.

An unhealthy diet is one that is high in fat, sugar and salt, and low in dietary fibre. Research has shown there are links between this type of diet and obesity, high blood pressure, coronary heart disease, cancer and tooth decay.

A **healthy balanced diet** contains a variety of types of food. It includes:

- lots of fruit and vegetables
- lots of starchy foods, such as wholemeal bread and wholegrain cereals
- some protein-rich foods, such as meat, fish, eggs and lentils
- some milk and dairy foods.

FACT

The Scientific Advisory Committee on Nutrition (SACN) is an advisory committee of independent experts that provides advice to the Food Standards Agency and Department of Health, as well as to other Government agencies and departments.

KEY TERMS

Food Standards Agency a UK government body that deals with food issues

Healthy balanced diet a diet containing a variety of types of food in the right proportions to promote good health

The Food Standards Agency is a government body that gives advice on healthy eating and food safety, and makes available research on nutrition, food safety and food related issues.

8 tips for eating well

Here are the **Food Standards Agency**'s 8 tips for eating well:

- base your meals on starchy food
- eat lots of fruit and veg
- eat more fish
- cut down on saturated fat and sugar
- try to eat less salt – no more than 6 g a day
- get active and try to be a healthy weight
- drink plenty of water
- do not skip breakfast.

Current dietary guidelines

This table shows the summary of the guidelines and programmes for health.

INVESTIGATION

Carry out some research on the web to find a range of campaigns that have been created to help people eat more healthily. You can choose campaigns from the UK and other parts of the world.

Present your findings in a short PowerPoint® presentation.

Guidelines and programmes for health	Summary
8 tips for eating well	Shows in a simple way how to eat healthily.
5 A DAY	Encourages us to eat plenty of fruit and vegetables.
The eatwell plate	Gives guidelines on the range and proportion of foods we need for a balanced diet.
Dietary Reference Values	Clear guidelines with specific recommendations for our needs at different ages.
Licence to Cook	Helps students to cook and learn the nutritional value of the food they are making.

QUESTIONS

1. What is meant by a healthy diet?
2. Give two tips from the 8 tips for eating well.
3. Give three reasons why the Licence to Cook programme will help people to eat more healthily.

5 A DAY campaign

The **5 A DAY** campaign, developed by the Department of Health, encourages us to eat five portions of fruit and vegetables a day. The average person in the UK eats less than three portions of fruit and vegetables a day, instead of the recommended five. Almost all fruit and vegetables count towards your 5 A DAY.

WEBSITES

5 A DAY, by the NHS

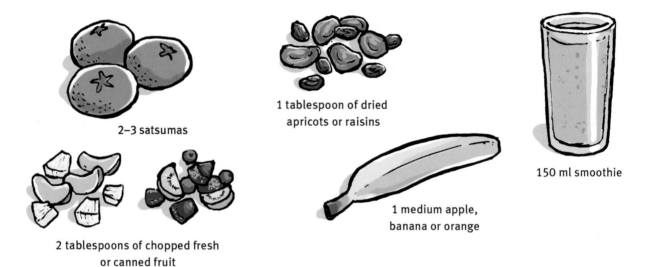

2–3 satsumas

1 tablespoon of dried apricots or raisins

150 ml smoothie

2 tablespoons of chopped fresh or canned fruit

1 medium apple, banana or orange

What is a 5 A DAY serving? 2–3 satsumas, 1 medium banana, orange or apple, 2 tablespoons of chopped fresh or canned fruit, 1 tablespoon of dried apricots, raisins, 150 ml smoothie.

Nutrition in fruit and vegetables

Fruit and vegetables are good sources of dietary fibre and **antioxidants**. Here are five reasons to eat five portions of fruit and vegetables a day.

1. They're packed with vitamins and minerals.
2. They can help you to maintain a healthy weight.
3. They're an excellent source of fibre and antioxidants.
4. They help to reduce the risk of heart disease, stroke and some cancers.
5. They taste delicious and there's so much variety to choose from.

How much is a portion?

For this campaign, a portion of fruit and vegetables is about 80 grams. Fresh, frozen, chilled, canned, 100 per cent juice and smoothies all count, as do dried fruit and vegetables. Fruit and vegetables don't have to be eaten on their own

TO DO

Keep a diary of food and drink that you eat for a week. Each day, make a list of the fruit and vegetables that you ate – in any form – and check if you are eating five a day.

Does your weekly food intake meet the 8 tips on eating well? (See page 3.) If not, what needs improving?

to count. You can include any vegetables found in soups, stews, sandwiches and other dishes.

Potatoes and other related vegetables such as yams and cassava do not count. This is because they are classified as starchy foods.

What's in a portion?

All fruits and vegetables contain a variety of vitamins and minerals. The main nutrients are shown in the table below.

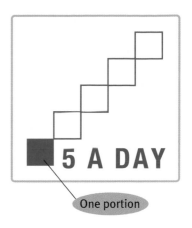

One portion

This logo is found on food packaging and shows how many portions of fruit and vegetables are in the food.

Fruit and vegetables	One portion – 80 g	Source of
Banana	1 medium banana	potassium
Orange	1 orange	Vitamin C
Avocado	Half an avocado	Vitamin E, B6, potassium
Beans	3 tablespoons of most beans	Fibre and iron
Broccoli	2 spears	Vitamin C
Carrots	3 heaped tablespoons if grated	betacarotene
Tomatoes	1 medium tomato, 7 cherry tomatoes, 2 canned tomatoes	Vitamins C and A, potassium

KEY TERMS

5 A DAY campaign a government campaign encouraging us to eat five portions of fruit and vegetables a day

Antioxidants chemicals found in vitamins A, C and E that help to protect the body from disease

5 A DAY food labels

Some food packaging with the 5 A DAY logo shows how many portions of fruit and vegetables a typical serving of the food contains. Each filled-in square of the portion indicator represents one portion.

TO DO

Create a recipe for a family dish that provides two portions of fruit and/or vegetables in a serving portion. You will need to weigh the ingredients carefully. Remember: one portion is 80 g.

QUESTIONS

1. What is the 5 A DAY campaign?
2. What is the recommended weight of a portion of fruit and vegetables?
3. Give two advantages of eating fruit and vegetables.

The eatwell plate 1

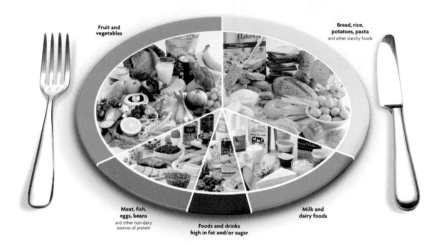

The eatwell plate with the five food groups.

WEBSITES

Food Standards Agency

The **eatwell plate**, from the Food Standards Agency, shows the proportions of the different food groups we should eat to maintain a healthy and well-balanced diet.

There are five food groups:

1. bread, rice, potatoes, pasta and other starchy food
2. fruit and vegetables
3. milk and dairy foods
4. meat, fish, eggs, beans and non-dairy sources of protein
5. food and drinks high in fat and/or sugar.

Try to choose options that are lower in salt when you can – adults should have no more than 6 grams of salt a day.

KEY TERMS

The **eatwell plate** a 'plate' diagram showing the proportions of the different food groups that we should eat to maintain a healthy and well-balanced diet

This table shows the food groups and choices that can be made.

Types of food in each food group					
Food group	1. Bread, other cereals and potatoes	2. Fruit and vegetables	3. Milk and dairy foods	4. Meat, fish and non-dairy sources of protein	5. Food and drinks high in fat and sugar
Types of foods in this group	'Other cereals' means things like breakfast cereals, pasta, rice, noodles. Beans and pulses form part of this group.	Fresh, frozen and canned fruit and vegetables and dried fruit. A glass of fruit juice. Beans and pulses form part of this group.	Milk, cheese, yogurt and fromage frais. This group does not contain butter, eggs and cream (see groups 4 and 5).	Meat, poultry, fish, eggs, nuts, beans and pulses. Beans include canned baked beans. Fish includes frozen and canned fish, fish fingers and fish cakes.	Margarine, butter, cooking oils, oily salad dressing, cream, chocolate, crisps, biscuits, cake, ice cream, rich sauces, sweets and sugar.
Main nutrients	Carbohydrate (starch) fibre, some calcium and iron, B vitamins.	Vitamin C, carotenes folates, fibre and some carbohydrate.	Calcium, protein, vitamin B12, vitamins A and D.	Iron, protein, B vitamins (especially B12), zinc and magnesium.	Some vitamins and essential fatty acids, but also a lot of fat, sugar and salt.

QUESTIONS

1. Give two examples for each of the five food groups on the eatwell plate.
2. List the main nutrients for each group.
3. Which groups do beans and pulses belong to?

Chapter 1

The eatwell plate 2

This table shows how to choose foods from the eatwell plate.

Food groups	1. Bread, other cereals and potatoes	2. Fruit and vegetables	3. Milk and dairy foods	4. Meat, fish and non-dairy sources of protein	5. Foods and drinks high in fat and sugar
How much to choose	Eat plenty; choose wholegrain varieties when you can.	Eat plenty, at least five portions of a variety of fruit and vegetables a day.	Eat some; choose lower-fat alternatives whenever possible or eat higher-fat versions infrequently or in smaller amounts.	Eat some; choose lower fat alternatives. Aim for at least two portions of fish a week, including a portion of oily fish.	Eat just a small amount.
What types to choose	Try to eat wholemeal, wholegrain, brown or high-fibre versions where possible.	Eat a wide variety of fruit and vegetables.	Lower-fat versions means semi-skimmed or skimmed milk, low fat 0.1% yogurt or fromage frais.	Lower-fat versions means meat with the fat cut off, poultry without the skin and fish without batter.	Some foods from this group will be eaten every day, but should be kept to small amounts.

Combination and composite food

Much of the food we eat is in the form of dishes or meals with more than one kind of food group in them. For example, pizzas, casseroles, pies, lasagne and sandwiches are all made with foods from more than one of the five food groups. These are called **combination** or **composite** foods.

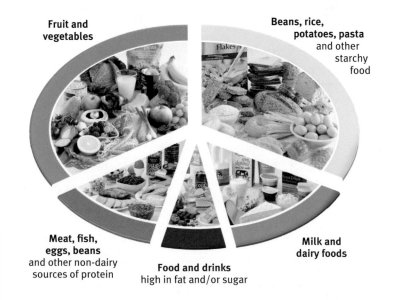

Fruit and vegetables

Beans, rice, potatoes, pasta and other starchy food

Meat, fish, eggs, beans and other non-dairy sources of protein

Food and drinks high in fat and/or sugar

Milk and dairy foods

Sections of the eatwell plate.

Bread is group 1

Cheese is group 3

Tomatoes are group 2

Burger is group 4

Combination foods, such as this quarter pounder, are made up of different food groups.

To make healthy choices, you need to identify the main food items or ingredients in combination foods and think about how these fit with the proportions shown in the eatwell plate.

Example

Here is an example of a combination dish.

Vegetarian chilli with rice made from tomato sauce, onions, red kidney beans and rice.

Which food belongs in which group?

Group 1	rice
Group 2	tomatoes, onions
Group 3	-
Group 4	red kidney beans
Group 5	-

So this dish has foods from groups 1, 2 and 4.

INVESTIGATION

Plan a day's meals including snacks and drinks. Show how your choice includes foods from the five food groups:

1. bread, rice, potatoes, pasta and other starchy food

2. fruit and vegetables

3. milk and dairy foods

4. meat, fish, eggs, beans and non-dairy sources of protein

5. food and drinks high in fat and/or sugar.

Test the nutritional value of the day's meals using a nutritional analysis program.

QUESTIONS

1. Which of the food groups should we eat lots of, and which should we eat only small amounts of?

2. Below are the ingredients for a pizza, which is a combination food.

   Pizza base with bread dough, topping with tomatoes, red peppers and cheese.

   How does it fit in the food groups? Complete a table like the one below.

   Which food belongs in which group?

Group 1	
Group 2	
Group 3	
Group 4	
Group 5	

Dietary reference values 1

Our energy and nutrient requirements vary according to age, gender, body size and levels of activity. As everyone is different, it is difficult to give exact information on individual energy and nutrient needs.

In the UK, estimated requirements for particular groups of the population are based on advice given by the Committee on Medical Aspects of Food and Nutrition Policy (COMA) in the early 1990s. This report provides standards that are used by nutritionists to help with detailed diet analysis.

Terms used

- **Dietary reference values (DRVs)** are a series of estimates of the amount of energy and nutrients needed by different groups of healthy people in the UK population. There are three types of estimate:
  - **Reference Nutrient Intakes (RNIs)** are used for protein, vitamins and minerals, and are an estimate of the amount that should meet the needs of most people.
  - **Estimated Average Requirements (EARs)** are used in particular for energy.
  - **Lower Reference Nutrient Intakes (LRNIs)** are for people with lower nutrient needs.

Nutrient requirements

The amount of each nutrient we need is called the nutritional requirement.

WEBSITES

Food Standards Agency

British Nutrition Foundation

KEY TERMS

Dietary reference values (DRVs) a series of estimates of the amount of energy and nutrients needed by different groups of healthy people in the UK population

Reference Nutrient Intakes (RNIs) an estimate of the amount that should meet the needs of most people

Estimated Average Requirements (EARs) used in particular for energy

LRNI for people with lower nutrient needs

Website for the British Nutrition Foundation, a good source of healthy eating information and resources for schools.

The requirements vary between individuals and life stages.

Dietary recommendations	
Energy and nutrients	**Dietary recommendations per day**
Energy	EARs for energy vary with age, gender and level of activity
Protein	RNI is 55.5 g for men, 45 g for women
Total fat	No more than 35% of food energy
Saturates	No more than 11% of food energy

Carbohydrates of which:
    starch
    sugars – non-milk extrinsic sugars (NMEs)
	50% of food energy:
	    39% of food energy
	    11% of food energy

Dietary fibre	18 g NSP; 24 g AOAC (see page 40)
Vitamins and minerals	Each has its own dietary recommendation

Guideline Daily Amounts

Guideline Daily Amounts (GDAs) are found on some food labels and help you to plan a healthy balanced diet. They were developed by food manufacturers and supermarkets to help consumers make food choices. Each GDA is for an average adult. They are called guidelines because they are a guide, not a target.

The GDA label has five parts – calories, sugars, fat, saturates and salt.

	Women	**Men**
Calories	2000	2500
Fat	70 g	95 g
Sugars	90 g	120 g
Saturates	20 g	30 g
Salt	6 g	6 g

Spinach & ricotta pizza
Nutrition information

Typical values cooked as per instructions	Per 100 g	Per ½ pizza	% based on GDA for woman	Women	Men	Children (5–10 years)
Energy	1001 kJ	1977 kJ				
	238 kcal	470 kcal	23.5%	2000 kcal	2500 kcal	1800 kcal
Protein	9.3 g	18.4 g	40.9%	45 g	55 g	24 g
Carbohydrate	28.7 g	56.7 g	24.7 %	230 g	300 g	220 g
of which sugars	2.7 g	5.3 g	5.9%	90 g	120 g	85 g
of which starch	25.9 g	51.2 g	-	-	-	-
Fat	9.6 g	19.0 g	27.1%	70 g	95 g	70 g
of which saturates	3.7 g	7.3 g	35.5%	20 g	30 g	20 g
mono-unsaturates	4.0 g	7.9 g	-	-	-	-
polyunsaturates	1.8 g	3.2 g	-			
Fibre	2.3 g	4.5 g	18.8%	24 g	24 g	15 g
Salt	1.0 g	2.0 g	33.3%	6 g	6 g	4 g
of which sodium	0.40 g	0.79 g	32.9%	2.4 g	2.4 g	1.4 g

Guideline daily amounts

You may want to keep an eye on your **salt** intake as too much may increase your blood pressure.

It's important to watch your **calorie** intake, as without regular exercise too many may lead to weight gain.

A diet low in **fat**, particularly **saturated fat**, could help to maintain a healthy weight and a healthy heart.

To maintain a healthy lifestyle, we recommend aiming for at least 30 minutes of moderate exercise each day, such as brisk walking.

Guideline Daily Amounts are shown on a food label.

QUESTIONS

1. What is meant by the terms: DRV, EAR, RNI?
2. What is meant by the term Guideline Daily Amount? Give two reasons why this information is useful.

Chapter 1

Dietary reference values 2

Nutrient requirements

The table below shows the Estimated Average Requirements (EARs) for energy for males and females at different ages.

EARs for males and females at different ages		
	Male	**Female**
Age	**energy kcal**	**energy kcal**
0–3 months	545	515
10–12 months	920	865
1–3 years	1230	1165
4–6 years	1715	1545
7–10 years	1970	1740
11–14 years	2220	1845
15–18 years	2755	2110
19–49 years	2550	1940
50–59 years	2550	1900
60–64 years	2380	1900
65–74 years	2330	1900
75+ years	2100	1810

KEY TERMS

kcal a unit of energy; it is short for kilocalories (see page 14)

Reference Nutrient Intake (RNI) is the term used to show the amount of protein, vitamins and minerals required by most people – 97 per cent of the population.

People's dietary needs change with age.

TO DO

Work in groups and choose one nutrient each. Draw a graph to show how the nutritional needs change with age. Draw separate lines for male and female. Present your findings.

[Graph: vertical axis labelled "energy needs" with gridlines at 0, 500, 1000, 1500, 2000, 2500, 3000; horizontal axis labelled "years" with markings at 0, 10, 20, 30, 40, 50, 60, 70, 80]

This table shows the RNI values for protein, vitamin A, thiamin, vitamin C, calcium, iron and zinc for males and females of different age groups.

RNIs for males and females at different ages

Age	Protein g	Vit A mg	Thiamin mg	Vit C mg	Calcium mg	Iron mg	Zinc mg
Male							
1–3 years	14.5	400	0.5	30	350	6.9	5
4–6 years	19.7	400	0.7	30	450	6.1	6.5
7–10 years	28.3	500	0.7	30	550	8.7	7
11–14 years	42.1	600	0.9	35	1000	11.3	9
15–18 years	55.2	700	1.1	40	1000	11.3	9.5
19–49 years	55.5	700	1	40	700	8.7	9.5
50+	53.3	700	0.9	40	700	8.7	9.5
Female							
1–3 years	14.5	400	0.5	30	350	6.9	5
4–6 years	19.7	400	0.7	30	450	6.1	6.5
7–10 years	28.3	500	0.7	30	550	8.7	7
11–14 years	41.2	600	0.7	35	800	14.8	9
15–18 years	45.4	600	0.8	40	800	14.8	7
19–49 years	45	600	0.8	40	700	14.8	7
50+	46.5	600	0.8	40	700	8.7	7

Summary of chart

Nutrient	Changes with age
Protein	Protein needs increase and are highest during teenage years.
Vitamin A	Vitamin A needs are highest in men from 15 years onwards.
Thiamin	Thiamin is needed during teenage years and men need more than women of the same age.
Vitamin C	Adults need to eat about 40 mg of vitamin C.
Calcium	Calcium needs are high in teenage years, especially for boys.
Iron	Teenage girls and women have the highest requirements for iron.
Zinc	Zinc needs are highest in men.

QUESTIONS

Use the RNI table for protein, vitamins and minerals.

1. Choose three of the nutrients and explain what happens to our nutrient requirements as we get older.
2. What is the difference between the nutrient requirements for males and females during that time?

Energy from food 1

The energy value of food comes mainly from the macronutrients – fat, protein and carbohydrate (starch and sugar). Fat supplies almost twice the amount of energy as the same weight of protein or carbohydrate. Fat is said to be an energy-dense food since it provides a more concentrated source of energy. That is why people are advised to lower the fat in their food if they want to lose weight.

As a basic guide:

- 1 gram of fat provides 9 kcal
- 1 gram of carbohydrates a provides 4 kcal
- 1 gram of protein provides 4 kcal
- 1 gram of alcohol provides 7 kcal.

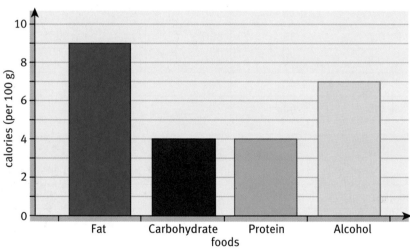

Energy from food.

Energy measurement

Energy is measured in **kilocalories** (kcal) and **kilojoules** (kJ). Nutritionists and dietitians tend to use kilocalories when they are planning diets for people.

Food labels show the kilojoule and kilocalorie energy value of the food product.

> 1 kcal = 1000 calories = 4.184 kJ
> 1 MJ (megajoule) = 1 million joules

WEBSITES

British Nutrition Foundation
Change4Life

KEY TERMS

Kilocalories/kilojoules measures of the energy value of a food product

Energy balance when energy in from food is the same as energy out from activities – it is the right amount of energy for our body needs

Why do we need energy?

Everything we do needs energy.

We need energy:

- to make our muscles move and carry out physical activity
- to maintain our normal body temperature
- to carry out the body's functions such as heartbeat, breathing and metabolism
- for tissue growth and repair.

Energy balance

The energy balance is the right amount of energy for our body needs. If we eat more food than we need, the excess is changed into fat. If we eat less than we need, and use up energy by taking exercise, the fat stores in the body are burnt as fuel and we may get thinner.

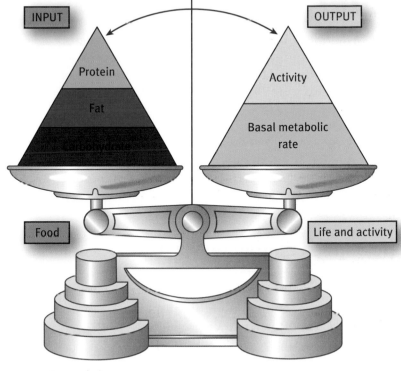

Energy balance.

To maintain a constant weight we need to balance the energy taken in as food with the energy burnt up as activity.

Input and output

The energy that we get from the food we eat is called input.

The energy that we use in our daily activities is called output.

To maintain body weight, energy input should be the same or less than energy output.

How does food produce energy?

The main nutrients in food are carbohydrates, fats and protein. Carbohydrates and fat are the main nutrients used for energy. Excess protein can be used for energy.

The Change4Life campaign helps us make changes to our diet and levels of activity. The campaign makes clear the link between fat and preventable illnesses.

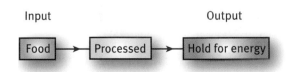

Food is processed by the body to release energy.

QUESTIONS

1. Why do we need energy from food?
2. Which nutrients provide energy?
3. How does the body release energy from food?
4. Why do some people become overweight?

Chapter 1

Energy from food 2

Carbohydrate is broken down into glucose, which is carried to body cells by the blood. We breathe in oxygen and this is carried to body cells. The glucose and oxygen combine to produce energy, water and carbon dioxide gas.

glucose + oxygen = water, carbon dioxide and energy

The energy can be used by the body for activity but, if energy is not needed immediately, it can be stored in the muscles and liver as **glycogen**. During exercise, when the body needs more energy, glycogen is broken down into glucose and then produces energy.

How much energy do we need?

We all need energy from food to keep us alive and active. The amount of energy we need varies with age, gender, body size and the amount of activity we carry out. The table on page 12 shows the energy requirements for different age groups.

Why do we have different energy needs?

Children are the most active and energy is needed for growth, so their energy increases as they get older. Adults need energy for activities; they have stopped growing and reached the maximum height, so body cells only require energy to function. Older people are generally less active and have stopped growing.

Children are active and need energy for growth.

Basal metabolic rate (BMR)

The **basal metabolic rate** is the amount of energy we need when the body is completely at rest and not moving about. This energy is needed to keep our body functioning and is used for breathing, blood circulation and other body processes such as digestion. The BMR accounts for two-thirds of a person's daily energy needs. The average BMR for men is 1600 kcal a day, and 1300 kcal for women.

Energy measurement

Our total energy needs are worked out by multiplying the BMR by the physical activity level (PAL).

EAR = BMR x PAL

KEY TERMS

Glycogen the form in which carbohydrate is stored in the body

Basal metabolic rate (BMR) the energy used when the body is at rest

The PAL scale goes like this:

- mostly inactive or sedentary (mainly sitting): 1.2
- fairly active (including walking and exercise once to twice a week): 1.3
- moderately active (exercise two to three times a week): 1.4
- active (exercise hard more than three times a week): 1.5
- very active (exercise hard every day): 1.7.

In the UK, the average physical activity level of most people is 1.4.

Energy use

Different activities use different amounts of energy. You can see from the table below that the lowest amount of energy is needed for sitting down, which is why we are advised to take exercise.

Different activities use up different amounts of energy.

Energy used in 20 minutes	
Activity	**Kilocalories used**
Running	210
Swimming	160
Jogging	140
Walking briskly	100
Cycling	140
Sitting	28
Football	160
Aerobics	120
Karate	140
Dancing	140
Tennis	140

TO DO

Use the table opposite showing energy requirements and draw a graph to show how energy needs change. Comment on your findings.

QUESTIONS

1. What is meant by basal metabolic rate?
2. Give examples of an activity that:
   a) has the highest energy needs
   b) has the lowest energy needs.

Overweight and obesity 1

Several health conditions and illnesses are linked to a poor diet. These include being overweight and **obesity**.

Obesity levels have tripled in England since 1980. If trends continue, by 2050, 60 per cent of men will be obese, 50 per cent of women and 25 per cent of young people and children. According to food surveys, we are eating less food than years ago, but we are not as active. So people are taking less exercise than they used to, which means they are eating more than they need for their energy requirements.

Obesity levels are increasing.

Why do people put on weight?

If we eat more food than we need for our normal activities, this food is stored as fat. For body weight to remain constant, energy intake must equal energy output. This is called the energy balance.

Health problems when overweight

Being overweight:

- increases the risk of coronary heart disease (CHD) and stroke
- may lead to an increased risk of certain cancers
- increases the risk of Type 2 diabetes – the risk is five times more likely in obese people
- places more strain on the hips, knees and back, can cause joint problems and can lead to osteoarthritis
- is linked with psychological problems; overweight people often feel unhappy.

Why do health risks increase with excess weight?

People who are overweight are more likely to have high blood pressure. High blood pressure increases the risk of CHD, which can lead to heart attacks. High blood pressure can also lead to strokes.

How do you know if you are overweight?

Body Mass Index, or BMI, is the method for estimating **body fat**. You can tell from your BMI whether you are overweight or obese.

WEBSITES

Food Standards Agency – use a BMI calculator

KEY TERMS

Obesity when someone has put on so much weight, it is dangerous for their health. It is caused by a combination of eating too many calories and not doing enough physical activity

Body Mass Index (BMI) a method for estimating body fat

Body fat fat stored in the body as glycogen (see page 16)

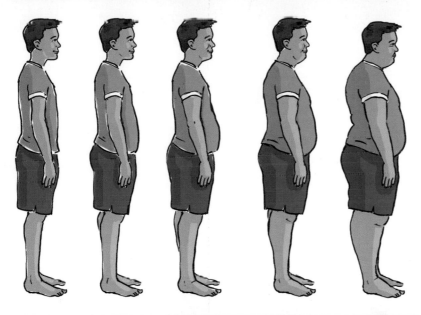

BMI shows if you are underweight or overweight.

BMI bands

Underweight	Healthy weight	Overweight	Obese
BMI less than 18.5	BMI 18.5–24.9	BMI 25–29.9	BMI 30–39.9
You are underweight and may need to gain weight.	You are an ideal weight.	You are overweight and should lose weight for the sake of your health.	This is very overweight and you are putting your health at risk.

Your BMI is calculated using the following equation:

your weight in kilogrammes (kg) divided by your height in metres (m) squared

So a man who weighs 85 kg and is 1.75 m tall will have a BMI of 28.

A BMI over 25 is defined as overweight, and over 30 is defined as obese.

A healthy weight check machine will check your BMI. It measures your BMI and body fat percentage, and a sensor notes your height. It will say whether you need to lose weight.

How to lose weight

In order to lose weight, you need to burn more calories than you take in from food and drink. You need to tip the energy balance by eating fewer calories and burning them off. Change4Life offers ideas about how to lose weight and eat more healthily.

QUESTIONS

1. What is meant by the term 'obese'?
2. Give two ways people can become overweight.
3. Name three health risks associated with being overweight.
4. Suggest ways that someone can try to lose weight.

Overweight and obesity 2

Ways to eat fewer calories

- Choose low-fat varieties of dairy and other products.
- Increase intake of starchy foods instead of fatty ones.
- Eat less of sugary foods.
- Increase intake of fruit and vegetables (aim to eat at least five portions a day).

WEBSITES

British Diabetic Association

Ways to eat fewer calories.

Sometimes certain medical conditions and drug treatments can cause weight gain, so people who are seriously overweight should see a doctor.

Portion sizes

Some foods are served in very large **portions**, which are high in calories. The government is encouraging food manufacturers to reduce the portion sizes of products. Healthier eating becomes easier if the tempting treats come in smaller packets.

Why do we overeat?

People often eat when they are not hungry, and so eat more than they actually need. Many people eat when they are bored or stressed. Treats such as high-fat cakes and sweet fizzy drinks can help cheer us up, but also provide extra calories.

'I'll have an extra large burger and fries.'

These days, food is easy to buy from shops and cafés. There is a lot of ready-prepared food for sale that may be high in fat and calories. It is very easy to eat foods high in fat and sugar as snacks or in drinks such as smoothies. Some families overeat and large portions of food are served at mealtimes.

'Junk food leaving people malnourished'

Why do young children become overweight?

Childhood obesity levels are determined before the age of five. Most excess weight is gained by a child before they start school and one in four children in England aged four to five are overweight, according to the latest figures.

The following is from a newspaper report commenting on the news that children are getting fatter.

Children learn how to eat by mimicking the things going on around them. In the early years, children are given food to eat, and if their mothers constantly give them food, they get used to snacking and eating throughout the day. Food is often given as a reward: 'You can have a bag of crisps if you sit quietly!' Food can be given to cheer children up: 'You can have a lollipop as you are so good.' This behaviour is learned at an early age, so food becomes a comfort and a reward. So, new mothers should be given advice and help to realise they can pass their views on food to their children. They need to learn that food is linked to emotional issues and not just providing food to eat.

KEY TERMS

Portions the sizes and weights of food we eat

INVESTIGATION

This activity involves some practical research into the size of portions of foods that we eat regularly. Find the calories in each portion and compare results.

- Weigh a medium portion of chips from a chip shop. Use a nutritional analysis program to find the number of calories in the portion.

- Find out the size of the largest milky coffee in a coffee shop, and use the Internet to find its calorie content.

- Find the largest can of sugary drink and get the calorie content for the can.

- What is the weight of a takeaway pizza that you might eat? Find the calories.

Which portion sizes surprised you? Prepare a report on your findings.

QUESTIONS

1. Suggest two ways that we can eat fewer calories.
2. Give three reasons why we can eat more food than we need.
3. Give your views on the article 'Why do young children become overweight?' Can you add any examples of your own where food is given as a reward or a treat?

Diet and health 1

Below are some health threats linked to a poor diet.

Heart disease

Coronary heart disease (CHD) is a preventable disease that kills more than 110,000 people in England every year (Department of Health). It is caused when the coronary arteries, which supply blood to the heart, become narrower. This is due to a build-up of fatty deposits in the arteries – called atherosclerosis. The artery may become so narrow that not enough blood gets to the heart. This means the heart muscle does not get the oxygen it needs, which produces pain and a condition called angina. If the narrowed artery becomes blocked by a blood clot, this causes a heart attack.

'Cardiovascular disease' includes all the diseases of the heart and blood vessels, including CHD, heart failure and stroke.

Things that increase the risk of developing heart disease include:

- high blood pressure
- high cholesterol levels
- not being physically active
- being overweight
- smoking
- diabetes.

Foods high in saturated fatty acids can raise blood cholesterol, which increases the risk of heart disease. Salt is also linked to coronary heart disease.

Foods high in fat such as this breakfast can raise blood cholesterol levels.

Diabetes

Diabetes is linked to heart disease, stroke, kidney failure and blindness. There are two types of diabetes: Type 1 and Type 2.

- **Type 1** is more likely to develop in younger people, but it can develop at any age. There are about 18,000 people under the age of 18 in the UK with Type 1 diabetes. With this type, the cells in the pancreas that produce insulin are destroyed. This type of diabetes is treated with insulin injections and diet.

- **Type 2** diabetes usually occurs in older people, but it is increasingly being found in younger people and children. This type of diabetes can be treated with diet and exercise alone, although people with Type 2 diabetes often need medication and insulin too. Type 2 diabetes often occurs in overweight people. As the number of obese people increases, the number of people with diabetes increases.

People with diabetes do not need to follow a special diet. They can follow the dietary guidelines for healthy eating for

FACT

There has been a large rise in the number of people in the UK with diabetes in recent years. Currently, 3.5 million people in Britain have diabetes, and 90 per cent of these have Type 2 diabetes.

everyone. Their diet should be high in starchy, fibre-rich foods and low in sugar and fat.

Bowel problems

These include constipation, piles (haemorrhoids), diverticular disease and bowel cancer.

- **Constipation:** The most common cause of constipation is a lack of dietary fibre and water in the diet. Faeces become hard, the abdomen is tender, and bowel movements are painful.
- **Piles or haemorrhoids:** These are swollen blood vessels around the anus that develop when people have constipation which causes strain on the system.
- **Diverticular disease:** This occurs when small pouches form in the large intestine. This is common in older people and the problem is linked to constipation. The disease can be treated with medicine, and a high fibre diet with plenty of fruit and vegetables can help. Good sources of fibre include some breakfast cereals, kidney beans, mixed unsalted nuts, wholemeal bread, baked beans, fruit and vegetables.
- **Bowel cancer:** There are many different causes of bowel cancer. It may be caused by genetics, which means the disease is inherited from people in the family. Research also suggests that a diet high in fat and red meat, and low in fibre, fruit and vegetables, can increase the risk of bowel cancer. Obesity has been linked to bowel cancer, so it is important to maintain a healthy weight. High alcohol consumption and lack of physical exercise have been linked to an increased risk of bowel cancer.

Regular exercise also helps with bowel problems.

Cancer

There are many types of cancer, but diet is thought to affect the risk of bowel, stomach and lung cancer. To avoid increasing our risk of developing cancer, we should eat a healthy balanced diet and adopt a healthier lifestyle. This means we should:

- eat more fruit and vegetables
- eat more starchy foods such as bread, pasta, rice, cereals and potatoes
- avoid eating highly salted, cured or smoked food
- drink alcohol in moderation (see pages 52–53)
- keep a healthy weight
- stop smoking.

A diet high in dietary fibre can help to prevent bowel problems.

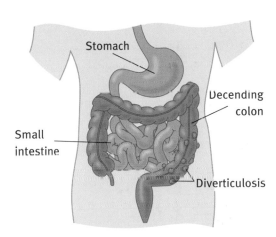

In diverticulosis, pouches form because of pressure on weak walls of the colon. In diverticulitis, these pouches may become inflamed.

QUESTIONS

1. What is:
   a) coronary heart disease
   b) cardiovascular disease?
2. Give two tips to help avoid these diseases.
3. Name the two types of diabetes.
4. What sort of diet should people with diabetes follow?
5. What foods should be eaten to help improve constipation and piles?

Diet and health 2

Anaemia

Anaemia is mainly caused by not having enough iron in the diet. Iron is needed for the formation of haemoglobin, which is found in red blood cells. It carries oxygen around the body to the cells to be used in energy release. Women and teenage girls need increased sources of iron when their periods start. Symptoms of anaemia include tiredness and delay in wound healing.

WEBSITES

Patient UK

Sugar and tooth decay

Dental plaque is a sticky film that clings to the teeth and contains bacteria. Bacteria use sugar for energy and produce acid, which attacks the tooth enamel and causes tooth decay – known as dental caries.

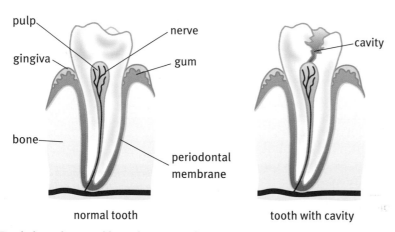

Tooth decay is caused by eating too much sugar.

Research shows that all types of sugar encourage tooth decay. Eating sugary foods throughout the day in the form of sweets and sugary drinks increases the risk of tooth decay. It is better to eat sugary foods at mealtimes instead, as this reduces the time the teeth are exposed to acid.

Ways to prevent tooth decay

- Cut down on sugary foods and drinks.
- Cut down on snacking between meals.
- Brush your teeth at least twice a day with fluoride toothpaste and visit the dentist regularly.
- Do not give babies and toddlers too much sweet food and drink.

Ways to prevent tooth decay include cutting down on sticky sugary foods and drinks.

Scurvy

This disease is due to lack of vitamin C. It was the cause of illness and death when sailors went on long voyages and had no fresh fruit. Elderly people may not eat enough and so could suffer from scurvy.

Rickets and osteomalacia

Vitamin D helps the absorption of calcium. Calcium is deposited in the skeleton when a child is growing. If the diet is low in calcium, the bones become thin and weak. Legs may become bowed causing a condition called rickets.

Osteomalacia is an adult disease where the bones demineralise and become weak. This can be caused by a diet low in vitamin D.

Health problems that can be linked to poor diet	
Unhealthy aspect of diet	**Health problems it may cause**
Eating lots of sugary foods and drinks	Tooth decay – dental caries
A diet high in salt	Raised blood pressure
A diet low in dietary fibre	Constipation and bowel-related illnesses
Overeating	Obesity and becoming overweight, with its related problems
Diet high in saturated fat	Raised blood cholesterol, which can lead to heart disease
Diet low in vitamin D	Can make bones and teeth brittle and weak
Diet low in vitamin B12	A type of anaemia
Diet low in folic acid	Folic acid-deficient anaemia
Diet low in iron	Iron deficiency – anaemia
Diet low in calcium	Can make bones and teeth brittle and weak
Too little water	Dehydration

INVESTIGATION

In the developed world, many of our dietary problems are due to overeating or eating the wrong types of food. In the developing world, many people often do not have enough food to eat. Carry out some research to find out about health issues in some of these countries. Interview people and find out their views on ways to solve the problem of shortage of food around the world.

Parts of the developing world have too little food.

QUESTION

Name a health condition that may be caused by:

a) a low iron intake

b) a high intake of sticky sugary foods

c) a diet low in vitamin C

d) a diet low in calcium and vitamin D.

Digestion

Food must be digested so that the nutrients in it can be absorbed into the bloodstream and used for energy, growth and body functioning.

What happens to food during digestion?

- Proteins are changed to amino acids.
- Carbohydrates are changed to **monosaccharides** – glucose, fructose and galactose.
- Fats are changed to fatty acids and glycerol.
- Minerals and vitamins pass into the blood stream unchanged.
- Dietary fibre cannot be digested and passes out of the body in the faeces.

KEY TERMS

Monosaccharide the simplest form of carbohydrate molecules

Enzyme a protein that speeds up a chemical reaction but is not used up in the process

Emulsify help fat and oil disperse in very fine droplets

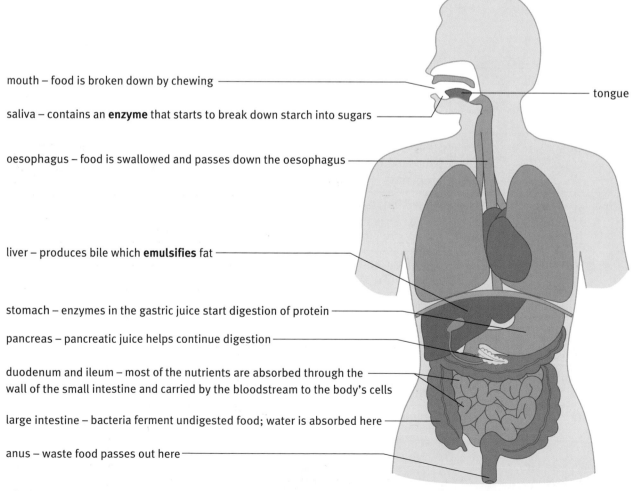

mouth – food is broken down by chewing

tongue

saliva – contains an **enzyme** that starts to break down starch into sugars

oesophagus – food is swallowed and passes down the oesophagus

liver – produces bile which **emulsifies** fat

stomach – enzymes in the gastric juice start digestion of protein

pancreas – pancreatic juice helps continue digestion

duodenum and ileum – most of the nutrients are absorbed through the wall of the small intestine and carried by the bloodstream to the body's cells

large intestine – bacteria ferment undigested food; water is absorbed here

anus – waste food passes out here

The digestive system.

What happens to different nutrients during digestion	
Digestive organ	**What happens there**
Mouth	Food is chewed into small pieces and mixed with saliva. Starch changes to maltose and dextrin.
Oesophagus	Food is pushed down the oesophagus into the stomach.
Stomach	Food is churned and mixed with gastric juice. Pepsin is an enzyme that starts to break down protein.
Small intestine	Food passes into the small intestine where digestion is completed and nutrients absorbed into the blood stream. Bile made by the liver emulsifies fat so that it can be digested. Enzymes in the intestine complete digestion.
Large intestine	Water is absorbed from food, leaving faeces.

Absorption of nutrients

After digestion the nutrients pass through the walls of the small intestine into the bloodstream. Most nutrients, except fatty acids and glycerol, are carried to the liver, which controls their distribution around the body. Undigested food that contains dietary fibre and bacteria passes into the large intestine, where water is absorbed. The faeces that remain are passed out of the body through the anus.

When food is eaten the nutrients are used for different body processes.

How nutrients are used by the body	
Protein	Replacement, repair and growth of body tissues
Carbohydrate	Used for energy
Dietary fibre	Provides bulk to the diet and helps eliminate waste products
Fat	Used for energy and essential fatty acids form cell membranes
Minerals and vitamins	Used for body processes
Liquid in food	Really important for all body cells to function

QUESTIONS

1. Give two reasons why food must be digested.
2. What happens to these nutrients when they are digested?
   a) proteins
   b) carbohydrates
   c) fats.
3. What happens to dietary fibre during digestion?

Macronutrients: Protein

There are five main groups of nutrients: protein, fat, carbohydrate, vitamins and minerals. **Macronutrients**, which include protein, fat and carbohydrate, are those nutrients that are needed in larger amounts; **micronutrients**, like vitamins and minerals, are needed in smaller amounts.

What are proteins?

Proteins are made up of long chains of building blocks called amino acids. These amino acids are made of the elements carbon, oxygen, hydrogen and nitrogen, and sometimes sulphur and phosphorus. There are 20 amino acids that make up proteins.

Our bodies can make eleven amino acids called non-essential, or dispensable, amino acids. We need to obtain the other nine **essential** (or indispensable) **amino acids** from our diets. Foods containing all essential amino acids are found in meat, offal (see page 84), fish, milk, cheese and eggs. Some vegetable proteins may not contain all the essential amino acids.

Function of protein

Every cell in the body contains some protein. Protein is needed for growth and repair of body tissue, muscles and blood cells. If we eat more protein than we need, the excess is used as a source of energy.

Daily requirements for protein	
Age	RNI for protein
Male 15–50 years	55.5 g
Female 15–50 years Pregnant woman Breastfeeding woman	45 g 51 g 56 g

Sources of protein

Protein sources from animal origin include meat, fish, poultry, eggs, milk, and milk products such as cheese and yogurt. These foods contain all of the essential amino acids and are said to have a high biological value (HBV).

Protein sources from plants include peas, beans, lentils, cereals, such as rice, wheat, flour, pasta, nuts and seeds.

KEY TERMS

Macronutrients foods such as protein, fat and carbohydrate, which are needed in larger amounts

Micronutrients vitamins and minerals that are needed in smaller amounts

Essential amino acids amino acids that have to be eaten, as the body cannot make them

TO DO

Plan a two-course meal that will provide 18 g of protein – about one-third of the daily needs of adults. Use a nutritional analysis program to show evidence of your choice of foods. Make and test the meal.

FACT

For vegans, a varied diet based on plant foods including peas, beans and lentils will meet protein needs. These foods are rich in protein and high in the amino acid lysine, which is low in many grains, nuts and seeds.

These foods tend to lack one of the essential amino acids and are said to have a low biological value (LBV). However, soya beans contain all of them.

Research shows that the body has a short-term store of amino acids and, if a variety of foods is eaten during the day, the body will have a sufficient supply of the essential amino acids.

Complementary proteins

Mixtures of plant protein can complement each other by supplying the full range of amino acids needed by humans. Vegetarian meals often supply two complementary proteins if grains and pulses are used, or a range of dairy products. Examples include rice and dhal (lentils), beans on toast, and pizza. Combining these two types of protein is called 'complementation of protein'.

Increasing the protein in dishes

If someone has a poor appetite or is a fussy eater, you may want to increase the protein in their meals. For example, you can add dried milk powder or grated cheese to potato or soups.

Fish, meat, eggs, nuts and seeds are good sources of protein.

Nutrition information

Ingredients: macaroni cheese (36%), salad (27%), apple pie (18%), custard

Nutrition information	per 100g	per portion	GDA (women)	GDA (men)	GDA (5-10yr)	traffic light
Energy (kj)	669.4 kj	3682.0 kj	43.9%	35.1%	48.8%	
Energy (kcal)	159.8 kcal	879.0 kcal	43.9%	35.1%	48.8%	
Protein	4.5 g	24.8 g	55.2%	45.1%	103.5%	
Carbohydrate	14.6 g	80.7 g	35.1%	26.9%	36.7%	
Fat	9.4 g	52.0 g	74.3%	54.7%	74.3%	●

net weight: 550 g   **allergens:** milk, wheat, wheat gluten, egg

You can test the amount of protein in a meal. This meal of macaroni cheese, salad, apple pie and custard supplies 24.8 g protein, which is high.

QUESTIONS

1. Why does the body need protein?
2. What happens if you eat too much protein rich food?
3. What are high biological and low biological value proteins?
4. Why do you think pregnant and breastfeeding women need more protein?

Macronutrients: Fats 1

What are fats?

Fats are a macronutrient, as they make up a large part of our diet. Fats are made up of carbon, hydrogen and oxygen. Fats can be hard fat and oils, which are liquid at room temperature. All fats provide 9 kcalories per gram. Too much fat in the diet can make us fat.

Fat is in many foods.

Functions of fat

- Fat supplies us with a concentrated source of energy.
- Fat is needed for structure of all body cells.
- Fat provides us with fat-soluble vitamins A, D, E and K.
- Body fat is stored under the skin and helps us keep warm.
- Fat provides us with essential fatty acids such as omega 3.

How much fat should we eat?

In the UK, we need to cut down on our fat intake, particularly saturated fat. Fat should supply no more than 35 per cent of our total food energy.

Sources of fat

Fat can come from:

- animal sources – butter, lard, milk, cheese, meat, oily fish, cream
- plant sources – vegetable oils, margarine, nuts and seeds.

Fats can be **saturated** or **unsaturated**.

Saturated fats

Most saturated fats come from animal sources and can be bad for our health. No more than 11 per cent of our food energy should come from saturated fat. Sources of saturated fat include butter, hard cheese, lard, coconut oil, palm oil, and fat in meat and pastry.

Unsaturated fats

Unsaturated fats include monounsaturated and polyunsaturated fats. These fats can reduce cholesterol levels. Most of us should aim to replace some of the saturated fat we eat with these good fats. Sources of unsaturated fats include olive oil, rapeseed oil, margarines and fats made from monounsaturated fat.

KEY TERMS

Saturated fats fats that come from animal sources and can be bad for our health

Unsaturated fats fats thought to be beneficial to our health

Trans fats similar to saturated fats in their effect on health

Sources of saturated fat.

Sources of polyunsaturated fat.

Trans fats

Trans fats (or trans fatty acids) are linked to coronary heart disease, which can lead to health conditions such as heart attacks and strokes. Trans fats are chemically altered vegetable oils. They are produced artificially in a process called hydrogenation, which turns liquid oil into solid fat.

Biscuit giant removes trans fat to make biscuits more popular

Essential fatty acids

Essential fatty acids must be obtained directly from foods as the body cannot make them. Examples include linoleic and alpha linoleic acids.

Omega 3 and omega 6 fatty acids

Omega 3 fatty acids can help to prevent blood clotting so they help in preventing coronary heart disease. They may also help prevent joint diseases. Sources of omega 3 fatty acids include fish oils – especially those from oily fish such as herrings and salmon. In the UK, we need to eat more oily fish. Omega 6 fatty acids help to prevent coronary heart disease. Sources include sunflower oil, corn oil and soya oils.

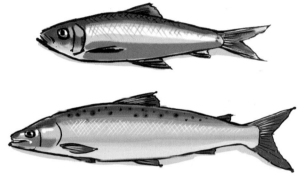

Omega 3 fatty acids are found in fish oil.

Cholesterol

Cholesterol is found in our blood and the food that we eat. Our bodies make cholesterol and it is part of all body cells and hormones. High blood cholesterol is thought to be one of the risk factors in the development of heart disease. To reduce blood cholesterol, we need to cut down on the total fat that we eat, especially saturated fats.

Some foods are designed to lower cholesterol.

QUESTIONS

1. Name two functions of fat.
2. Why should we cut down on the amount of fat we eat?
3. What is meant by:
   a) saturated fat
   b) unsaturated fat?
4. Why are the following fatty acids important?
   a) omega 3
   b) omega 6.

Macronutrients: Fats 2

Fat and coronary heart disease

Coronary heart disease (CHD) is a major cause of death in the UK. Major risk factors include smoking, raised cholesterol levels, a high fat diet, high blood pressure, lack of exercise, obesity, family history of heart disease, stress, and increasing age. To reduce the risk of CHD, we should eat less fatty food and increase the amount of fibre rich, starchy foods and fruit and vegetables. More exercise can help too.

How much fat?

Check the amount of fat in food by reading the nutrition label, which shows the fat in 100 grams and a portion. Some labels show the amount of saturated fat.

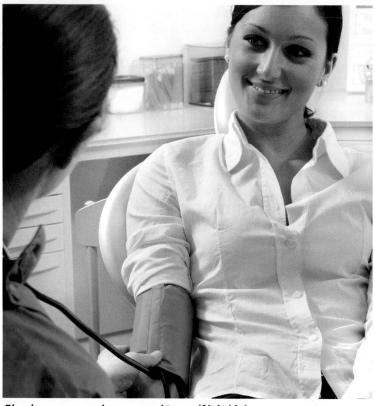

Blood pressure can be measured to see if it is high.

Amount of fat and saturated fat in 100 grams of high fat and reduced fat foods		
100 grams food	Fat in grams	Saturated fat in grams
Mayonnaise	79	6.6
Light mayonnaise 60% less fat	30	3
Full fat soft cheese	24	16
Soft cheese, lighter in fat	11.5	7.6
Butter	81.7	54
Flora Light spread	38	9.3
Lard	100	44
Olive oil	91	15

Hidden fat is fat that you cannot see in a food product. High-hidden fat products include chocolate bars, cheese, fried snack foods and pizzas.

Some tips for reducing fat in the diet

What to do	How to do it
Eat fewer fatty foods.	Avoid chips, sausages, pastry pies and puddings, fried food.
Try cooking with less fat.	Use non-stick frying pans and only use a little fat if frying.
Cut down on fried or roasted food.	Grill, boil, steam or bake instead.
Do not eat cheese too often.	Eat smaller portions of cheese.
Remove fat from meat and chicken.	Drain off fat from roasted meat and remove fatty chicken skin.
Cut down on fatty snacks.	These include cakes, biscuits, chocolate, doughnuts, crisps and tortilla chips.
Avoid butter and margarine that are high in fat.	Use lower fat spreads.
Choose lower fat versions of foods.	Examples include semi skimmed milk, reduced fat yogurt, lower fat cream cheese.
Skim the fat from gravies, soups and stews.	Spoon off fat from the top when the mixture is cooling down.
Try not to add fat to vegetables.	Do not add butter to boiled vegetables.

Reduced fat foods.

INVESTIGATION

Make a collection of food labels and arrange them in order, starting with the highest fat content first. You could get people to guess which foods are the highest and lowest in fat.

QUESTIONS

1. What habits can increase the risk of coronary disease?
2. What is meant by the term 'hidden' fat?
3. Look at the table on the previous page showing fat in food.
   a) Which two foods have the highest fat content?
   b) Which two foods are highest in saturated fat?
4. Give reasons for choosing the lighter-fat versions of some foods.

Macronutrients: Carbohydrates

Carbohydrates are a macronutrient, as we need them in large quantities.

What are carbohydrates?

Carbohydrates are made up of carbon, hydrogen and oxygen. Carbohydrates provide energy. During digestion, carbohydrates are changed to glucose, which is used for energy. Excess glucose is converted into fatty acids and stored as body fat.

There are two types of carbohydrate.

- **Starch:** a polysaccharide made up of glucose units. It is partly digested in the mouth and changed in the small intestine to glucose.
- Sugar: including sucrose (table sugar), glucose, fructose (found in fruit), maltose and lactose (found in milk).

Glucose is quickly digested and provides instant energy.

Sources of carbohydrate

Starches – found in bread, pasta, rice, potatoes, pulses and breakfast cereals.

Sugars – found in fruits, soft drinks, table sugar, sweets and cakes.

How much carbohydrate should we eat?

We should increase the amount of starchy, fibre-rich foods in our diet and reduce the sugary foods. Starchy foods should make up at least 50 per cent of our food energy intake. Eating more starchy foods helps to cut down the fatty foods in our diet, as starchy foods fill us up.

Carbohydrate-rich foods.

How much of our energy should come from carbohydrates?

Here are the DRVs – Dietary Reference Values – for sugars and starches.

Nutrient	Target
Carbohydrates	Up to 50% of food energy
Of which non-milk extrinsic sugars (NMES)	No more than 11% of food energy
Of which starches	About 39% of food energy

Non-milk extrinsic sugars (NMES) are found in table sugar, sweets, sugary drinks and cakes.

Glycaemic index

The **glycaemic index** (GI) is a measure of the effects of carbohydrates on blood glucose levels. Carbohydrates that break down quickly during digestion and release glucose rapidly into the bloodstream have a high GI. Carbohydrates that break down slowly, releasing glucose gradually into the bloodstream, have a low GI. Foods with a low GI have health benefits. Eating low-GI foods throughout the day can help keep your blood glucose levels stable while providing lasting energy.

GI type	Foods
Low GI foods	Most fruit and vegetables, grainy breads, pasta, legumes/pulses, milk
High GI foods	Cornflakes, baked potato, watermelon, croissant, white bread, sweets

QUESTIONS

1. Name two functions of carbohydrates.
2. What are the two types of carbohydrate? Name a good source of each one.
3. How much of our food energy should come from:
   a) NMEs
   b) starch?
4. What is meant by the term 'glycaemic index'?

Macronutrients: Starches

Starches

We must eat more starchy food. Starches are called **complex carbohydrates**. They are polysaccharides that are made up of glucose units.

KEY TERMS

Complex carbohydrates polysaccharides that are made up of glucose units, including starch

Examples of starchy foods.

Eat more starchy foods

A diet high in starchy foods is very healthy and helps to keep blood sugars at a constant level. Eating more starchy foods helps to cut down on the amount of fatty food we have in our diet. Starchy foods help to fill us up and so we are less likely to eat high-fat snacks.

Important sources of starchy food include pasta, rice, bread, breakfast cereals, potatoes and pulses. They provide other nutrients as well as starch.

Nutrients in starchy foods					
	Good source of starch	**Source of fibre**	**Source of protein**	**Other nutrients**	**Other points**
Potatoes	✓	✓		Vitamin C	Gluten free
Bread	✓	✓	✓	B vitamins, calcium	
Pasta	✓	✓	✓	B vitamins	
Rice	✓	Some	✓		Gluten free
Pulses – lentils	✓	✓	✓	Vitamin A	High in protein

Most starchy food contains some fibre. Some foods contain more fibre than others.

- **High in dietary fibre** – wholemeal bread, beans, lentils, high fibre breakfast cereals, wholemeal pasta, wholemeal flour.
- **Lower in dietary fibre** – white bread, white pasta, cornflakes, white flour, white rice.

INVESTIGATION

Plan a meal that includes plenty of starch. Aim to use starchy foods that are also high fibre and nutritious, such as bread, potatoes and pasta.

Use a nutritional analysis program to compare the starch content of different foods. Remember that starchy foods often need added water when they cook, so compare the cooked version of these ingredients.

Work out the nutritional value of the meal and find out how much starch one person might eat in the meal.

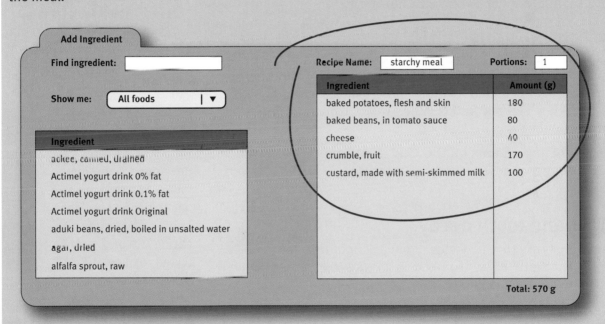

Plan a meal with plenty of starch – this is the meal choice.

QUESTIONS

1. Why should we eat more starchy foods?
2. What other nutrients are found in these starchy foods?
   a) potatoes
   b) bread
   c) rice
   d) pasta.
3. Suggest two ways that people could eat more starchy foods in their diet.

Macronutrients: Sugars

Intrinsic and extrinsic sugars

Intrinsic **sugars** are those contained in the structure of foods such as sugars from fruits. Extrinsic sugars are those sugars added to foods such as biscuits. Sugars are found naturally in milk, honey and fruit.

How much sugar should we eat?

We should cut down on the amount of **non-milk extrinsic sugars (NMEs)** to less than 11 per cent of our total food energy intake. This type of sugar is found in table sugar, honey, sweets, sugary drinks, cakes and biscuits and also in processed food. Table sugar is said to provide 'empty' calories, as it provides energy but no extra nutrients.

Hidden sugar in food

Food manufacturers add sugar to many food products to improve the taste and flavour. These sugars provide empty calories. Sugar is added to soups, pasta sauces, canned fruit and breakfast cereals, and is called hidden sugar because we may not realise it is in the food.

Look at the ingredients on the food label and sugar may be listed as sugar, glucose, dextrose, fructose, glucose syrup and invert sugar.

Sugar and tooth decay

Research shows that all types of sugar encourage tooth decay. To prevent tooth decay we need to cut down on sticky sugary foods and sugary drinks between meals. For more on sugar and tooth decay see page 24.

Change4life is a campaign to help us eat more healthily and be more active.

They have a sugar swap initiative, where they persuade people to change to less sugary foods. Here are their suggested sugar swaps.

Drink swap

Switch from sugary drinks to 'no added sugar' drinks such as water, milk, unsweetened fruit juice or even sugar-free fizzy drinks.

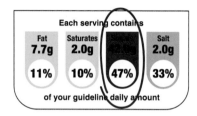

Each serving contains			
Fat	Saturates		Salt
7.7g	**2.0g**		**2.0g**
11%	**10%**	**47%**	**33%**

of your guideline daily amount

Sugar is shown on a food label.

Snack swap

Choose snacks without added sugar such as fruit, unsalted nuts, breadsticks, rice cakes or toast, instead of sweets, biscuits, chocolate, cakes and pastries.

Food label swap

When shopping, compare food labels and switch to the one that's marked lower in sugar or sugar free. Some packaging uses a traffic light system (see page 50) which makes it even easier to choose food that is lower in sugar. Go for more 'greens' and 'ambers' and fewer 'reds' in your shopping basket.

Breakfast swap

Switch to lower sugar cereals or other breakfast options like fruit or toast – but if you spread on jam or honey, make sure it's a thin layer!

Dessert swap

Switch from sugary desserts like chocolate, biscuits and cake to less sugary desserts, like yogurt or fruit. Or compare the labels on two desserts and choose the one with the lower level of sugars.

Ways to reduce sugar intake

- Use less sugar in your recipes – there are reduced sugar products you could use.
- Choose fruit instead of sugary snacks such as sweets.
- Try using artificial sweeteners instead of sugar.
- Choose low-calorie and sugar-free products.
- Use fruit canned in natural juice rather than sugar.
- Choose sugar-free drinks.

INVESTIGATION

Make a collection of food labels and find ones with hidden sugars. Make a list of the types of sugar used to sweeten the foods. Suggest ways that the food could be made with less sugar. Write a report or create a PowerPoint® presentation on your findings.

Levels of sugar in food may be cut to reduce obesity

QUESTIONS

1. What is meant by NMEs?
2. Why do sugary foods encourage tooth decay?
3. Suggest two ways to reduce the amount of sugar you eat.

Dietary fibre

The term 'dietary fibre' describes a number of different substances such as **non-starch polysaccharides (NSP)**, oligosaccharides and lignin. It also includes a number of other associated plant substances, such as resistant starch.

Dietary fibre cannot be digested by the body, so is not classed as a nutrient. It is found mainly in cereal foods, beans, lentils, fruit and vegetables.

High-fibre foods.

Types of dietary fibre

There are two types of NSP – insoluble and soluble.

- **Insoluble fibre** absorbs water and increases in bulk. This helps the faeces become soft and bulky, and keeps the gut in good working order.
- **Soluble fibre** is thought to slow down digestion and absorption of carbohydrates, and helps to control blood sugar, which helps to stop us feeling hungry.

According to the American Association of Analytical Chemists (**AOAC**) definition, fibre includes lignin and resistant starch as well as NSP.

Function of dietary fibre

Dietary fibre cannot be broken down during digestion, although micro-organisms that live in the large intestine can digest fibre.

Dietary fibre:

- helps to prevent constipation and disorders of the digestive system
- helps to lower blood cholesterol and glucose levels
- adds bulk to faeces, which helps to eliminate waste matter from the body
- decreases the rise in blood glucose after a meal.

A low-fibre diet is linked with constipation and gut diseases such as diverticulitis and bowel cancer.

KEY TERMS

Non-starch polysaccharide (NSP) contains insoluble and soluble fibre

AOAC fibre fibre as defined by the American Association of Analytical Chemists, including a lignin and resistant starch

Englyst method a method of fibre analysis used for NSP measurement

Nutrition information

Ingredients: red kidney beans (41%), rice (21%), leeks (10%), oil, onions, pepper, salt, garlic clove

Nutrition information	per 100 g	per portion	GDA (women)	GDA (men)	GDA (5-10yr)	traffic light
Energy (kJ)	674.9 kJ	1,633.3 kJ	19.5%	15.6%	21.7%	
Energy (kcal)	161.8 kcal	391.6 kcal	19.5%	15.6%	21.7%	
Protein	3.7 g	9.0 g	20.1%	16.4%	37.7%	
Carbohydrate	15.4 g	37.4 g	16.2%	12.4%	17.0%	
Total sugars	2.8 g	6.7 g	7.5%	5.6%	7.9%	◐
Fat	9.8 g	23.8 g	34.1%	25.1%	34.1%	●
Saturated fat	1.2 g	2.9g	14.6%	9.7%	14.6%	◐
Fibre	3.2 g	7.9 g	33.0%	33.0%	52.9%	
Salt	0.7 g	1.7 g	29.0%	29.0%	43.5%	●
Sodium	287.6 mg	696.0 mg	29.0%	29.0%	43.5%	

net weight: 968 g   **allergens:**

A veggie burger provides 7.9 g fibre per portion.

How much dietary fibre should we eat?

In the UK, most people do not eat enough fibre. The average intake is 12 g per day. The recommended intake for adults for non-starch polysaccharide (NSP) is 18 g per day. Younger children need less.

If the AOAC method is used, the advised intake is 24 g.

Fibre claims on food labels

Foods and food products that contain 6 g fibre per 100 g can be labelled as a 'high-fibre' food.

Fibre measurement

In the UK, the Englyst method is used for dietary fibre measurement. This method measures only the non-starch polysaccharides (NSP), a type of carbohydrate associated with plant cells that includes cellulose and plant gums.

Other EU countries and the USA, Canada and Australia use the AOAC method. This method includes lignin and resistant starch, which are not classified as NSP.

The AOAC method is used by manufacturers on labels. For many foods, using the AOAC method will give higher values of fibre compared to the Englyst method. Scientists believe that the AOAC method overestimates the amount of functional dietary fibre in the food and nutritional label. So a review will take place to consider the definition of fibre and what measures to use on labels.

Ways to increase fibre

- Choose whole cereals such as wholegrain breakfast products.
- Use nuts and seeds, which are very high in fibre.
- Beans, lentils and peas can be added to savoury dishes.
- Dried fruit such as apricots, figs and prunes contain fibre.

Eating more fibre can cut the risk of breast cancer in pre-menopausal women, according to scientists. A study found that women with a high intake of fibre – particularly wholemeal bread and wholegrain cereals – cut their risk of breast cancer in half.

nutritional information		
typical values	100g	as sold
Energy kJ	1,630	
kcal	366	
Protein	10.8g	
Carbohydrate	59.2g	
- of which sugars	12g	
Fat	9.5g	
- of which saturates	1.7g	
- mono-unsaturates	3.5g	
- polyunsaturates	4.3g	
Fibre	7.4g	
Salt	below 0.1g	
- of which sodium	below 0.1g	

Fibre on a food label. A portion of this muesli provides 7.4 g fibre, which is 30 per cent of GDA recommendation.

TO DO

Find a recipe for the main course of a meal and use a nutritional analysis program to find the amount of fibre in 100 grams. Try to increase the fibre in the dish by adding higher-fibre ingredients. Make the dish and find the new fibre content in 100 g.

'Fibre reduces breast cancer risk'

QUESTIONS

1. What is dietary fibre?
2. Give two functions of dietary fibre.
3. Give three examples of foods that are high in fibre.
4. Suggest two ways you could persuade an adult to eat more fibre.

Micronutrients: Vitamins 1

Remember that a healthy, balanced diet gives us all the vitamins and minerals we need.

Vitamins and minerals are called micronutrients since they are needed in smaller quantities compared with the requirements for the macronutrients (protein, carbohydrate and fat). The report *Dietary Reference Values for Food Energy* shows the quantities of vitamins and minerals recommended for people of different ages.

Vitamins may be divided into water-soluble and fat-soluble.

- **Water-soluble vitamins** – B vitamins and vitamin C dissolve in water, and tend to be excreted every day in urine. This means they need to be eaten regularly.

KEY TERMS

Antioxidants chemicals found in vitamins A, C and E that help to protect the body from disease

WEBSITES

British Nutrition Foundation

Water soluble vitamins	Use by the body	Source
Vitamin B1 – thiamin, riboflavin	Helps the release of energy from carbohydrates. Needed for normal growth in children. Functioning and maintenance of nerves.	Red meat, liver, milk, fortified breakfast cereals, potatoes, bread, pasta and yeast extracts.
Vitamin B2 – riboflavin	Helps the release of energy from carbohydrates. Needed for normal growth in children.	Red meat, liver, milk, fortified breakfast cereals, and yeast extracts.
Vitamin B3 – niacin	Helps the release of energy from carbohydrates.	Red meat, liver, milk, fortified breakfast cereals and yeast extracts.
Vitamin B6 – pyridoxine	Needed for the metabolism of protein and formation of red blood cells.	Red meat, liver, fortified breakfast cereals, potatoes, eggs and yeast extracts.
Vitamin B12 – cobalamin or cyanocobalamin	Helps the formation of red blood cells. Anaemia can result with formation of incorrect blood cells. May be deficient in vegetarian diet.	Red meat is major source. Found in foods of animal origin such as milk, meat and eggs and yeast.
Vitamin B – folate (found in foods in natural form) or folic acid when added to food	Important for the formation of blood cells. Recommended in the early stages of pregnancy to prevent neural tube defects such as spina bifida.	Found in yeast extract, leafy green vegetables such as spinach, peas and cabbage, fruit such as oranges. Bread is often fortified with folate.
Vitamin C – ascorbic acid	Increases the absorption on non-haem iron. Haem iron is found in meat. Maintains body's connective tissue, important for wound healing.	Fruit – especially citrus fruit including oranges and lemons. Vegetables – especially green vegetables and tomatoes.

Water-soluble vitamins can be stored in the body in the liver.

- **Fat-soluble vitamins** – usually be stored in the body.

Vitamins A, C and E are called the **antioxidant vitamins.** Antioxidants help protect the body from disease. Studies show that the risk of heart disease is reduced if you eat higher levels of vitamins A, C and E.

Foods rich in vitamin C.

Water-soluble vitamins

The B group vitamins include thiamin, riboflavin, niacin, B6, B12 biotin and panthothenic acid.

Other vitamins

Folate (or folic acid) is essential for many body processes, including the production of red blood cells. Most people can get all the folate they need from a healthy, balanced diet and they do not need to take supplements containing folic acid.

Folate is needed for the development of the unborn baby. It helps the rapid cell division and growth that takes place during pregnancy and reduces neural tube defects, such as spina bifida, in the unborn baby. Women who are trying to get pregnant, or who are pregnant, should take a 400 microgram (mcg) supplement of folic acid every day from the time they stop using contraception until at least the 12th week of pregnancy.

Antioxidants

Antioxidants are naturally occurring chemicals in foods that help to counter the harmful effects of free radicals, which have been linked to the development of several diseases including cancer and heart disease.

Fortified breakfast cereals are rich in B vitamins.

INVESTIGATION

Carry out some research using the Internet to find out more about antioxidants and how they can help prevent diseases. Write a short report on your findings. Include some ways we can increase these types of food in our diet.

QUESTIONS

1. Name two water-soluble vitamins.
2. What are the functions of each of these vitamins?
3. Give one source of each of these vitamins.
4. Which vitamin is needed to help iron absorption?
5. Which foods contain this vitamin?

Micronutrients: Vitamins 2

Fat-soluble vitamins

Vitamin A (retinol and carotene) is important for night vision, and helps to maintain skin and other tissues. Vitamin A as retinol is found only in animal foods such as butter and fortified foods such as margarine. Carotene is found in red and orange vegetables and green leaves.

Foods rich in vitamin A.

Vitamin D works with calcium, and helps bone formation and repair. The dietary source of vitamin D is animal foods, but exposure to sunlight ensures that most people have an adequate supply. Vitamin D in a vegan diet is obtained mainly from fortified food such as margarine.

Foods rich in vitamin D.

FACT

Very high doses of betacarotene, which the body converts to vitamin A, may cause cancer, so people are advised not to take betacarotene supplements, to try to help protect against cancer. Eating lots of fruit and vegetables will provide plenty of betacarotene in the diet.

Vitamin	Use by the body	Sources
Vitamin A – retinol	Formed by the body from betacarotene. Needed for night vision by making visual purple. Helps maintain healthy skin. Helps keep the mucous membranes free from infection. Needed for normal growth in children.	Found in full fat milk, cheese, eggs, oily fish, liver and butter. Added to margarine and spreads. Formed from betacarotene and found in carrots, spinach, cabbage and yellow fruit.
Vitamin D – cholecalciferol	Works with calcium to form healthy bones and teeth.	Most people get vitamin D from the action of sun on the skin. It is added to low fat spreads and margarines. Lean red meat is good source of vitamin D.
Vitamin E – tocopherol	Antioxidant that helps to protect the body from disease. Needed for healthy membranes. Evidence shows it may help to prevent heart disease and cancer.	Widely available and found in polyunsaturated oils, margarine, sardines, nuts and seeds, egg yolk, milk.
Vitamin K	Correct blood clotting and bone metabolism.	Formed by the body in the intestine. Found in leafy green vegetables, red meat, cereals and oils.

Vitamin E appears to be important in preventing heart disease.

Vitamin K is needed for blood clotting, and is thought to be important in bone metabolism and the prevention of osteoporosis.

INVESTIGATION

Find out which foods have been fortified with vitamins and minerals. You can do this research using the Internet or by visiting supermarkets. Look at the ingredients listed on food products and you will see the vitamins and minerals listed on the label.

You may see claims on the packet.

QUESTIONS

1. Name two fat-soluble vitamins.
2. What are the functions of each of these vitamins?
3. Give one source of each of these vitamins.
4. Which vitamin is needed to work with calcium to form bones?
5. Which foods have this vitamin added to them?

Micronutrients: Minerals 1

Minerals are micronutrients because they are needed in small amounts. Remember that a healthy, balanced diet gives us all the vitamins and minerals we need.

Your body needs small amounts of minerals to grow and stay healthy. Minerals have three main functions, which are:

- building strong bones and teeth
- controlling body fluids
- turning food into energy.

Essential minerals include calcium, iron, magnesium, phosphorus, potassium, sodium, chlorine and zinc. Other minerals needed in small amounts include copper, selenium and iodine.

Foods rich in calcium.

Calcium

Calcium combines with phosphorus to make calcium phosphate, which makes bones and teeth hard and strong. Calcium helps blood clotting and muscle functioning. Calcium absorption is controlled by vitamin D, so we need to eat calcium-rich foods with a vitamin D supply – from food or sunlight.

Sources of calcium

Good sources of calcium include milk, cheese and other dairy foods, leafy green vegetables, soya beans, tofu and soya drinks with added calcium.

Calcium deficiency in children can lead to bones and teeth that are not properly formed. Rickets is a disease where the leg bones bend with body weight. In adults, osteomalacia has been linked with poor calcium absorption.

TO DO

Design and make a meal for a family and show how you have increased the amount of calcium-rich foods in the meal. Test out your findings using a nutritional analysis program.

KEY TERMS

Deficiency of a mineral when the mineral is in poor supply in the diet

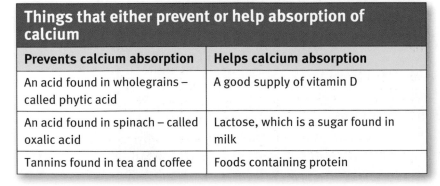

Things that either prevent or help absorption of calcium	
Prevents calcium absorption	**Helps calcium absorption**
An acid found in wholegrains – called phytic acid	A good supply of vitamin D
An acid found in spinach – called oxalic acid	Lactose, which is a sugar found in milk
Tannins found in tea and coffee	Foods containing protein

Alpro soya drink is fortified with calcium.

Osteoporosis

Osteoporosis is a disease where the bones become fragile, lose bone mass, become porous and can break. It is more common in women, when bone loss increases after menopause, when their hormone levels change.

To help avoid osteoporosis:

- increase foods that contain vitamin D, calcium and phosphorus
- take more exercise to strengthen bones.

Phosphorus

Phosphorus works with calcium, and is essential for healthy bones and teeth. Phosphorus is present in all foods from plants and animals, and the normal diet will supply sufficient phosphorus for our needs.

Iron

Iron helps to make haemoglobin in the red blood cells, which carry oxygen from the lungs to body tissue. There are two forms of dietary iron: haem iron and non-haem iron. Red meat has haem iron, which is easy to absorb.

Good sources of iron include liver, meat, beans, nuts, dried fruit, whole grains, fortified breakfast cereals, soyabean flour and most dark green, leafy vegetables.

Requirements for iron

- Adult men need 8.7 mg of iron a day.
- Adult women need 14.8 mg.

Low iron levels

A lack or **deficiency** of iron in the diet can lead to iron deficiency anaemia. Symptoms include tiredness, lethargy and difficulty concentrating. Young or pregnant women are most at risk of iron deficiency anaemia. Young women need an iron-rich diet, because this is the time they start their periods.

FOODS RICH IN IRON

- Offal & red meat
- Dark green vegetables
- Pulses & whole-grain cereals
- Nuts & seeds
- Fortified breakfast cereals

Foods rich in iron.

Young or pregnant women are most at risk of iron deficiency anaemia.

Prevents iron absorption	Helps iron absorption
Phytic acid found in wholegrains	A good supply of vitamin C
Oxalic acid found in rhubarb and spinach	
Tannins found in tea and coffee	

QUESTIONS

1. What is the function in the diet of:
   a) calcium
   b) iron?
2. Give two reasons why we need to eat:
   a) calcium-rich foods
   b) iron-rich foods.
3. Give three sources of foods that contain:
   a) calcium
   b) iron.
4. Name two substances that block iron absorption.

Micronutrients: Minerals 2

These are some important minerals found in food.

Magnesium

Magnesium is needed to develop the skeleton and for nerve functioning. It is found in cholorophyll, the green plant colour. It is also found in meat, wholegrains, nuts and seeds.

Deficiency – may well lead to hypertension and cardiovascular disease.

Potassium

Potassium is involved in the fluid balance of the body. A diet high in potassium can help reduce the effects of sodium and so help to lower blood pressure. Potassium is needed for heart muscle function. The main dietary sources of potassium are fruit and vegetables, and potassium is also found in salt substitutes, coffee and potatoes.

Deficiency – people are rarely deficient in this mineral.

Zinc

Zinc is important for the immune system to help fight diseases and infection. It is also needed for wound healing and normal growth. Zinc is found in meat, dairy products, pulses and wholegrain cereals.

Deficiency – this is rare but may lead to poor growth in children.

FOODS RICH IN ZINC

- Meat
- Dairy products
- Pulses and wholegrain cereals

Foods rich in zinc, which is needed for growing children.

Selenium

Selenium is an antioxidant and protects against heart disease. Selenium is found in red meat, fish and cereals. Brazil nuts are a source of selenium. Extra selenium is needed during breastfeeding and **lactation**.

Deficiency – this is rare in the UK, but may affect the thyroid function and lower resistance to infection.

Fluoride

Fluoride is essential for hardening teeth enamel and preventing teeth from decaying. It makes teeth more resistant to acids produced by the bacteria in the mouth. Fluoride is found naturally in tea and sea fish, and is added to the water supply in parts of the country.

Fluoride toothpaste can supply fluoride.

Deficiency – this is rare, though excess fluoride can lead to discolouration or mottling of the teeth.

Fortification of foods

Food fortification means adding nutrients such as minerals and vitamins to food products to help make sure that these nutrients are in our diet. Foods fortified by law include margarine, which is fortified with vitamins A and D.

Why fortify foods?

In countries where intakes of certain nutrients are very low, fortification can help to reduce nutrient deficiency diseases. One example is the addition of iodine to salt to decrease iodine deficiency disorders.

Fortified foods make an important contribution to diets in the UK. Examples include breakfast cereals, which are fortified with iron and calcium, and white and brown flour, which are fortified with calcium. Some soya drinks are fortified with calcium too. Folic acid is added voluntarily to bread and breakfast cereals.

KEY TERMS

Lactation producing milk after pregnancy

Food fortification adding nutrients to food products

INVESTIGATION

Look at a collection of food labels from breakfast cereals and margarines and find which ones have been fortified. Read some of the claims on the labels and write a short report on your findings.

QUESTIONS

1. What are the functions in the diet of:
   a) magnesium
   b) potassium
   c) zinc
   d) selenium?
2. Give one source of each of these minerals.
3. Why are foods fortified with nutrients?
4. Which foods are fortified with minerals?

Salt and sodium

Sodium

Sodium helps to maintain the fluid balance of the body and functions with potassium and chloride. Sodium is needed for nerves and muscles to function.

Excess sodium in the diet is linked to high blood pressure. Sodium is lost in sweat.

Chloride is found in body tissues and is needed for body functions. It is found in table salt.

Salt

Salt is sodium chloride. We are advised to keep our salt intake under 6 g a day.

Salt and health

High salt intake can lead to raised blood pressure and the increased risk of heart disease and stroke.

Foods high in salt.

A lot of ready-to-eat foods contain salt. You can find out how much there is in a portion by reading the label.

Some labels show the traffic light system for the salt content. If the label is red, then you should only eat small amounts of this food.

Salt content in 100 g	
Green	Less than 0.3 g
Amber	More than 0.3 but less than 1.5 g
Red	More than 1.5 g

FACT

In the UK, 75 per cent of the salt we consume is already in the food we buy.

Cutting 0.5 g salt from people's daily diet would save 3,500 lives each year in the UK.

Some labels show the salt content on the Guideline Daily Amount column. This has a limit of 6 grams of salt a day for adults and 4 grams a day for children aged 5–10 years.

This is the nutrition label for a veggie burger. The salt is red, which means it is high.

Nutrition	Per 100 g	Per burger	% based on GDA for adult
Energy	593 kJ, 141 kcal	676 kJ, 161 kcal	8.1%
Protein	20.5 g	23.4 g	52.0%
Carbohydrate	3.5 g	4.0 g	1.7%
Fat	5.0 g	5.7 g	8.1%
Fibre	3.4 g	3.9 g	16.3%
Salt	1.5 g	1.7 g	28.3%

— high in salt

Ways to cut down on salt

- Read food labels to see the amount of sodium and salt they contain, then choose lower salt products.
- Avoid ready-made foods that are high in salt. This is shown as red in the traffic light on the food label.
- Use stock cubes and soya sauce with care, as they contain salt.
- Cook with less salt, using herbs, spices and lemon juice instead to add flavour.
- Cut down on salty snacks, sauces and pickles.
- Use fewer salty meat products – avoid sausages, beefburgers and pies.
- Use low salt alternatives to season foods.

TO DO

Create a breakfast from sausages, bacon, egg and bread with some margarine. Work out the amount of salt and then the total the breakfast provides of the GDA.

Create a breakfast that is lower in salt.

Amount of salt in foods		
Food	Amount of salt in the portion	Percentage of the GDA
One beef sausage	0.7 g	12%
Rasher of bacon	0.8 g	13%
One egg	0 g	0%
Slice of bread	0.35 g	6%
10 g margarine	0.1 g	1.5%

QUESTIONS

1. What is salt made from?
2. What health problems are linked to eating too much salt?
3. Suggest ways in which people can reduce their salt content.

Water and alcohol

Water

Water is essential for life, but is not a nutrient. Most foods contain water, especially fruit and vegetables. You can drink water from the tap, and most drinks, including milk, are made of water.

Functions of water

Water is a major constituent of all body fluids, measuring about 70 per cent. Water helps to:

- digest and absorb nutrients
- remove waste products from the body
- control body temperature
- your concentration
- lubricate joints and membranes
- prevent **dehydration**.

We lose water in hot weather and when we exercise. Water is also lost through sweat, urine, faeces and breathing. This water needs to be replaced. Dehydration occurs if we lose water from the body and do not replace it.

How much fluid do we need?

In the UK, we need 1.2 litres of fluid (six to eight glasses) every day to stop us getting dehydrated.

Water in schools

There have been campaigns to provide fresh drinking water to primary and secondary students in schools. The aim is to encourage students to drink water during the day in place of sugary, fizzy drinks.

Alcohol

In the UK, alcohol intake is measured in units. Each unit is equivalent to around 10 ml or 8 g of pure alcohol.

A small glass of wine is approximately 1.5 units; half a pint of beer is approximately 2 units. The government's guidelines say that:

- a man should not regularly drink more than three to four units a day
- a woman should not regularly exceed two to three units a day
- 'an alcohol-free childhood is the healthiest and best option. However, if children drink alcohol, it should not be until at least the age of 15'.

Water is Cool in School

Do you want to:
- be cool
- do better at sports
- have more energy
- have fresher breath
- avoid headaches
- be healthy

Then **drink water** regularly throughout the day

Why not carry a water bottle with you? ...coming soon from a tap near you!

Water is Cool in School campaign.

FACT

Water contains no energy in the form of kcal/kJ.

WEBSITES

Water is Cool in School

Alcohol guidance (NHS)

KEY TERMS

Dehydration when the body is short of water

Binge drinking when people drink excessive amounts of alcohol in a short time

In Great Britain, about one-third of men (31 per cent) and one in five women (20 per cent) drink more than the advised weekly limits of 21 and 14 units a week.

Health risks linked to alcohol

Short-term health risks from excess alcohol include:

- anxiety
- sexual difficulties such as impotence
- impaired judgement leading to accidents and injuries
- loss of consciousness
- suffocation through choking on your own vomit
- potentially fatal alcohol poisoning.

Heavy drinkers and **binge drinkers** increase their calorie intake, which can lead to obesity. Long-term illnesses include damage to an unborn child, liver disease, osteoporosis (thinning of the bones), pancreatitis, stomach ulcers, infertility, heart disease, raised blood pressure, stroke, dementia and brain damage. The good news is that, when you reduce your drinking, the symptoms improve.

A unit of alcohol is...

FACT

Nearly 33,000 people in the UK die from alcohol related causes each year – that is ten times as many people as die on the roads every year.

Binge Britain

5,000 children a year now being treated for drink problems

In 2007 the number of under 18s admitted to hospital through alcohol was 8,494 – no fewer than 23 a day.

QUESTIONS

1. Give three functions of water in the body.
2. What is meant by dehydration?
3. Why is water better to drink than sugary, fizzy drinks?
4. Give an example of a drink that is one unit of alcohol.
5. Name two health risks associated with excess alcohol intake.
6. Give two reasons why you think binge drinking is increasing.

ExamCafé

Welcome

There are many facts to learn in this section. You need to know details of the eatwell plate, dietary guidelines and our energy balance. You also need to understand information on the macro and micronutrients. You will see much of the information is in tables.

Practise the questions at the end of each spread. Then think of your own and test them on a friend.

Revision

Revision checklist for nutrition and health

Copy and complete the table below to show the things you need to learn for each topic. List three or four key things to learn in each box.

Spread heading	Things to learn
Current dietary guidelines	Healthy balanced diet, 8 tips for eating well, 5 A DAY
The eatwell plate	
Dietary reference values	
Energy	
Overweight and obesity	
Diet and health	
Digestion	
Macronutrients: Protein	
Macronutrients: Fats	
Macronutrients: Carbohydrates	
Macronutrients: Starch	
Macronutrients: Sugars	
Dietary fibre	
Micronutrients: Vitamins	
Micronutrients: Minerals	
Salt and sodium	
Water and alcohol	

Exam tips

For many of the questions, you need to recall information that you have learned.

- Read and interpret the questions carefully.
- Focus on the key words that tell you what is required.
- Look at how many marks are awarded for each part of the answer.
- To get higher marks make sure you answer with enough information to get the marks.

Examples

Here are some examples of questions and suggested answers.

Question 1

Why is it important to include dietary fibre in the diet?
(2 marks)

Answer

Remember you need to give two answers to get full marks.

- To prevent constipation.
- To prevent disorders of the digestive system.
- To add bulk to increase waste matter.

Question 2

Discuss the nutritional value of including fruit and vegetables in the diet. (4 marks)

Answer 2

Remember you need to provide four points for full marks.

- High in dietary fibre.
- Low in calories.
- Rich in vitamins and minerals.
- Some contain antioxidants.
- They help reduce the risk of heart disease, strokes and some cancers.
- Vitamin C from citrus fruits helps in the absorption of iron.
- There is a wide range of fruit and vegetables which adds colour and flavour to meals and they can be eaten raw and cooked so a versatile, nutritional food.

Dietary needs: Age differences and pregnancy

Pregnancy

Pregnant women have increased requirements for energy and some nutrients to help keep themselves and the developing baby healthy. Pregnant women should not 'eat for two', as they may become overweight, but energy requirements do increase during the last three months of pregnancy.

Folic acid

If women want to become pregnant, they should take a supplement of folic acid to help prevent neural tube defects in their baby. A **neural tube defect** is called spina bifida, which affects the development of the spine and nervous system.

The pregnant woman's diet must contain sufficient protein, iron, phosphorus and vitamins to meet the needs of the mother and the growing baby. Protein is needed for growth and repair of the mother and unborn child. Iron is needed to form red blood cells and help prevent anaemia, which can lead to tiredness and ill health.

Vitamin A

Pregnant women should not eat too much vitamin A as it can harm the unborn baby. Eating a well-balanced diet provides all the vitamin A the body needs. Pregnant women should avoid liver or liver products such as pâté, as liver contains high levels of vitamin A. They should also check with a doctor before taking high-dose multivitamins or cod liver oil supplements, as these may also contain vitamin A.

Alcohol

The Department of Health advises that pregnant women, and women who are trying to get pregnant, should avoid drinking alcohol. Heavy drinking during pregnancy can lead to low birth weight and more serious birth defects.

Food choices during pregnancy		
Nutrient	**Why it is needed**	**Sources**
Starchy, fibre-rich food	Higher energy needs by about 200 kcal extra a day	Wholemeal bread and cereals
Vitamin D	Prevents low birth weight	Sunlight, oily fish, margarine
Folate	Prevents neural tube defects, spina bifida	Breakfast cereals and bread, green vegetables
Calcium	Helps growth of skeleton of foetus	Dairy foods, white bread, green vegetables
Iron	Helps with baby growth and prevents anaemia in mother	Red meat, green vegetables
Dietary fibre	Prevents constipation	Wholegrain products and vegetables
Protein	For baby's growth and mother's health	Meat, fish, eggs, cheese
Vitamin C	Helps iron absorption	Citrus fruits

Food poisoning

Listeria

Listeria is a food-poisoning bacteria that can cause serious illness in pregnant women, and may lead to miscarriage or early delivery of the baby. Listeria may be found in uncooked meats, uncooked vegetables, unpasteurised milk, foods made from unpasteurised milk, and some chilled foods. Pasteurisation destroys the bacteria, so during pregnancy, pasteurised foods such as pasteurised cheese can be eaten.

Salmonella

Pregnant women should avoid raw eggs or any foods that contain raw eggs because they may contain **salmonella**, which causes food poisoning. Salmonella is also found in raw poultry and raw meat. Pregnant women must take care to avoid eating food that may lead to food poisoning, which causes sickness and diarrhoea, and loss of valuable nutrition.

KEY TERMS

Neural tube defects problems in unborn babies that can lead to spina bifida

Listeria and **salmonella** food poisoning bacteria

QUESTIONS

1. Name two important nutrients that a pregnant woman needs for her health and the health of her baby.
2. Why is folic acid important in the diet of a pregnant woman?
3. Explain why listeria food poisoning is dangerous for pregnant women.
4. Name two foods that may contain listeria.

Chapter 2

Dietary needs: Babies

Breastfeeding

For the first six months, a baby's diet is just milk. Breast milk is the best food for babies, as babies grow very quickly and breast milk provides them with all the nutrients they need in the right proportions.

When women are breastfeeding, they need to make sure their diet contains foods that are good sources of energy, protein, calcium, phosphorus, magnesium and zinc, as well as B group vitamins and vitamins A, C and D. Energy needs increase during breastfeeding, as the mother has to produce breast milk. Constipation can be a problem during and after pregnancy, so the diet should contain foods that are good sources of dietary fibre.

WEBSITES

British Nutrition Foundation

Changes in energy needs of a pregnant and breastfeeding woman	
Lifestage	Calorie needs per day
Women 19–50	1940
Pregnancy – last 3 months	2140
Breastfeeding	2430

Advantages of breastfeeding

- The milk contains all the energy and essential nutrients that a baby needs.
- It is safe for the baby – made-up milk can be unhygienic if bottles and water are not sterilised, and this can lead to food poisoning.
- Breast milk contains antibodies that help to protect the baby from infections.
- It is easy for the baby to digest.
- It helps the mother and child to bond and form a relationship.
- Breast-fed babies are less likely to be overweight.
- Breast milk is free and convenient.
- Breastfeeding can help reduce the likelihood of allergic food reactions.
- It may help the mother to lose excess fat stores gained during pregnancy.

Formula milk

Specially modified infant formula milk has been developed for babies so that they can be bottle-fed. The bottles, teats and equipment must be thoroughly sterilised to prevent the baby becoming ill. Take care when preparing the milk and follow the instructions. An extra scoop of milk powder will make the milk too concentrated, and can lead to dehydration and overfeeding.

Weaning

When babies are weaned, they gradually begin to eat solid food, which is given from the age of six months. Giving a baby solid foods before they can cope with them can increase the risk of infection and allergies. Foods that are not suitable for babies under six months are: foods that contain wheat, gluten, eggs, fish, shellfish, liver, and soft and unpasteurised cheeses. A baby's immune system is too young to deal with foods that can cause allergies or foods that may contain harmful bacteria, such as the unpasteurised cheese.

Breast milk or formula milk should be given as the main drink until the baby is one year old. Cow's milk can only be given after the child is one year old.

Care during weaning

- In the early stages of weaning, avoid foods that contain gluten and nuts, in order to prevent allergies.
- Foods should be mashed or puréed to make them smooth – for example, puréed fruits and mashed bananas.
- Include cereals such as baby rice and maize, but not wheat, which contains gluten.
- Food should be nutritious but not high in fat.
- Do not add salt, honey or sugar to the food.
- Babies need a good supply of protein to help them grow, so use foods with egg, yogurt and milk.
- The baby's iron stores have been used up, so introduce foods that contain iron, such as minced-up red meat.
- Do not leave babies unsupervised when they are feeding, as they could choke.
- During teething, children can chew carrots or rusks but should not be given sugary sweet drinks outside of meal times.

KEY TERMS

Weaning when babies change over from milk to solid food

QUESTIONS

1. Give three advantages of breastfeeding a baby.
2. When is the best time to start weaning a baby?
3. Give three tips for food choices when weaning a baby.

Chapter 2

Dietary needs: Toddlers and young children 1

Young children need to follow a healthy diet so that they grow and stay active and healthy. They should be encouraged to try a variety of foods.

Children are growing very quickly and need good sources of all nutrients.

- Protein is needed for growth, repair and maintenance of body tissues.
- Starchy carbohydrates such as pasta, bread and potatoes should be the main source of energy.
- The minerals calcium, iron and phosphorus as well as vitamin D are needed for healthy bones and teeth.
- Iron is important for healthy blood, and children need this mineral along with vitamin C to help iron absorption.

High-salt and high-sugar foods should be limited.

Important nutrients needed by young children		
Nutrient	**Why it is needed**	**Sources**
Thiamin	Needed for energy metabolism	Red meat, liver, milk, fortified breakfast cereals
Energy from starchy carbohydrates	Growth spurt needs energy	Bread, pasta, rice, potatoes
Calcium	Needed for bone growth	Milk, cheese, green vegetables
Vitamin D	Works with calcium in bone formation	Sunlight, margarines
Iron	Needed for healthy blood	Meat, green vegetables
Protein	Children are growing fast	Meat, fish, eggs, milk, cheese

Tips for food choice for young children

- Try to give two to three servings a day of starchy foods such as potatoes, yams, rice or bread.
- Fruit and vegetables should be included at two or more meals each day.
- The child should have one serving a day of one of these foods – cooked meat, fish, egg, tofu or pulses such as beans or lentils.
- Red meat such as beef, lamb and pork is an excellent source of iron.
- Vegetarians can use iron-containing foods such as peas, beans and lentils.
- Eggs are a nutritious and cheap source of protein. They should be well cooked to avoid the risk of food poisoning.

Feeding young children

Some young children can be fussy eaters and refuse to eat certain foods. To encourage good eating habits, children should sit down at meal times and join in with family meals. Food should be attractive and easy to eat, and served in a child-sized portion as children have small appetites. Get children to try a variety of tastes and textures. Children should become independent and feed themselves as soon as possible.

A child's diet should be balanced. Meals should provide foods that contain protein, calcium and starchy ingredients – though be careful not to include too much fibre-rich food as this can be filling and children may not get the nutrients they need. Children should eat a variety of fruit and vegetables. They should not be given sugary drinks, or too many snacks between meals like sweets and crisps, which fill children up but have low nutritional value.

Hard foods such as carrots and apple can help to develop strong teeth and gums. Do not give young children large lollipops, gobstoppers or nuts, as they can choke on these foods.

INVESTIGATION

How can parents give a child a healthy diet that meets their energy needs?

- Plan a day's meals for a child and test it out on a nutritional analysis program. Does it provide enough energy and the range of nutrients that the child needs? If not, make changes and test again.
- Plan and prepare a meal that you could serve to a young child. Explain the reasons for your choice. How have you made the meal attractive to a young child? Show the nutritional value of the meal.

QUESTIONS

1. Name three nutrients that young children need and give one example of a food source of each nutrient.
2. Describe a lunchtime meal that could be eaten by a young child and give reasons for your choice.
3. Suggest three ways to encourage a young child to eat a healthy diet.

Dietary needs: Toddlers and young children 2

Ready-prepared baby foods

Some parents like to give their baby or toddler ready-prepared baby foods.

Advantages

- They are quick and easy to use, especially when in a hurry.
- A range of products is available, with a choice of tastes.
- Baby foods offer a range of nutrients and some have extra vitamins and minerals added.

Disadvantages

- They are more expensive than homemade food.
- They may not provide a full range of nutrients. In later stages of weaning, the baby may need to eat large amounts to meet their energy needs.
- Children's eating habits are set early – is eating ready-prepared food from a packet or jar to be encouraged?
- Parents do not experiment with their cooking and come to rely on these products.
- Babies and young children are not eating the same food as the rest of the family.

INVESTIGATION

Carry out a survey to find out the range of ready-prepared foods for young children. You can visit a supermarket or use the Internet. Keep a detailed record of your findings on a table like the one below so that you can compare costs.

Food	Description	When is it eaten	Cost and weight	Your views

Look at the food labels and nutritional value of the food. Now prepare some similar foods from scratch using fresh ingredients. Keep a record of the costs. Compare the tastes and costs, and write a report on your findings.

TO DO

This information is on a pack of vegetable fingers for children. Give your views on the advantages and disadvantages of this type of food.

> **Vegetable fingers**
> Fun fingers with carrots, peas and sweetcorn – watch your kids enjoy vegetables.
>
> **Description**
> Vegetable filling (72%), batter, breadcrumbs, vegetable oil.
>
> **Ingredients**
> Vegetable filling: vegetables (sweetcorn, carrots, peas), water, potato flake, egg white powder, salt, rice starch, yeast extract, onion powder, mustard.
>
> Batter: water, wheat flour, salt.
>
> Breadcrumbs: wheat flour, yeast, water, salt.

Teeth

The first teeth develop in a baby before birth so children need to learn from an early age how to care for their teeth. Sugar and sugary drinks are linked with **dental caries** – tooth decay.

Things that increase the chances of tooth decay in young children include:

- giving them drinks with added sugar, honey or fruit juices in bottles
- using feeding bottles with milk or sugary drinks for a long time
- giving them sugary foods and drinks throughout the day
- not brushing their teeth very often.

Ways to improve

- Stick to having sugary foods and drinks at mealtimes.
- Do not leave children to suck on feeding bottles or teats full of drink for long periods.
- Avoid sipping sugary drinks or sucking sweets too often. The longer the sugar is in contact with teeth, the more damage it can cause.
- Do not choose sticky foods such as toffee and chewy chocolate, which stay in the mouth for a long time.
- Encourage good dental hygiene – teach children to brush their teeth at least twice a day.
- Register with a dentist before problems occur and have regular check-ups.

KEY TERMS

Dental caries tooth decay

QUESTIONS

1. Give two advantages and two disadvantages of using ready-prepared baby food.
2. What are your views on ready-prepared baby foods?
3. Name three ways to help prevent a young child getting dental caries.

Dietary needs: Teenagers

Teenagers are growing faster than at any other life stage and so their nutritional needs are high. Adolescents also tend to be more active than in later life.

Protein is needed for this time of rapid growth, repair and maintenance of body tissues.

Energy requirements increase due to increased growth and levels of activity.

Iron is really important for teenage girls who have started their periods and need iron to prevent anaemia. Boys also need iron for their fast rate of growth.

Calcium and vitamin D are essential for this time of rapid bone growth.

TO DO

- Use the data from the table to write a report to show how the needs for protein, vitamin A, thiamin, vitamin C, calcium, iron and zinc change during teenage years.

- Suggest some important foods that can be part of the diet to make sure that teenagers have sufficient amounts of these nutrients.

Recommended Nutrient Intake (RNI) for males and females of different age groups							
Age	Protein g	Vit A ug	Thiamin mg	Vit C mg	Calcium mg	Iron mg	Zinc mg
Male							
7–10 years	28.3	500	0.7	30	550	8.7	7
11–14 years	42.1	600	0.9	35	1000	11.3	9
15–18 years	55.2	700	1.1	40	1000	11.3	9.5
19–49 years	55.5	700	1	40	700	8.7	9.5
Female							
7–10 years	28.3	500	0.7	30	550	8.7	7
11–14 years	41.2	600	0.7	35	800	14.8	9
15–18 years	45.4	600	0.8	40	800	14.8	7
19–49 years	45	600	0.8	40	700	14.8	7

ACTIVITY

- Design a day's menu for a teenager that will provide a range of the important nutrients that they need to keep healthy.

- Prepare and test a two-course meal that is inexpensive and quick to prepare and also is a good source of calcium and iron. Test this out on a nutritional analysis program.

You can see the changes that are needed for teenagers for the different nutrients.

The diet of teenage girls has been found to be low in iron and calcium. Many teenagers are also drinking excessive amounts of alcohol and smoking.

Important nutrients needed by teenagers

Nutrient	Why it is needed	Sources
Plenty of energy from starchy carbohydrates	Growth spurt needs energy, and increase in activities	Bread, pasta, rice, potatoes
Protein	Teenagers are growing fast and need protein for growth and repair of tissues	Meat, fish, eggs, milk, cheese
Calcium	Needed for bone growth and future bone health	Milk, cheese, green vegetables
Vitamin D	Works with calcium in bone formation	Sunlight, margarines
Iron	Needed for healthy blood, and blood is lost when teenage girls start their periods	Meat, green vegetables
Vitamin C	Helps iron absorption	Fruit and vegetables
Thiamin	Needed for energy metabolism	Red meat, liver, milk, fortified breakfast cereals
Zinc	Important for the immune system to help fight diseases and infection, and for male fertility	Meat, dairy products, pulses and wholegrain cereals

Anorexia nervosa

People suffering from the eating disorder **anorexia nervosa** – mainly teenage girls – restrict the amount of food they eat. Someone with this disorder becomes obsessed with losing weight and has a distorted view of their own body size. After a time, they become very thin. Sufferers need long-term specialist medical help, and support from family and friends.

KEY TERMS

Anorexia nervosa an eating disorder where people restrict the amount of food they eat

QUESTIONS

1. Give two reasons why some age groups need different amounts of energy.
2. Why do teenage girls need good sources of iron in their diet?
3. Why is calcium an important mineral for teenage boys and girls?

Dietary needs: Adults

Adults need a well-balanced diet and should not eat more food than they require for their energy needs. If they do, they will put on weight.

Food needs change with age.

- A baby needs nutritious food to help build its body and keep it healthy.
- Adolescents and young adults have high energy and nutritional needs because they are growing rapidly and are often very active. Their calcium requirements increase because they need to build strong bones.
- Older people need slightly less energy from food than they did in their middle years, as their **metabolism** is slowing down.

Factors other than age affect food needs too.

- Males tend to need more energy from food than females. This is because men are usually bigger than women and have more muscle tissue.
- Iron is needed by women to make up for iron lost from periods. So women require more iron than men.
- People who take a lot of exercise, or have physically demanding jobs, have greater energy needs than inactive people and those who sit down all day.

People's food needs change with age.

Older people

When people get older:

- they need less energy from food
- under-nutrition is more of a problem than for young adults
- they need smaller portions of **nutritionally dense foods**
- exercise is important to strengthen bones and muscles
- their senses of taste and smell change.

With age, the metabolism slows down, and people are not as active. Older people may get diet-related problems, such as bone and digestive problems. **Osteoporosis**, where the bones become fragile, is often found in older people.

Many elderly people may eat less because of chewing difficulties or general ill health. Older people often have increased nutritional needs because of disease or injury. Poor nutrition leads to a slower recovery from illness, increased risk of infection and poor healing. Nutritionally dense supplements can be used, especially if the older person has lost their appetite. Efforts should be made to prevent weight loss and malnutrition, to give older people a better quality of life.

TO DO

Design three lunchtime menus suitable for an older person. Show that your meals are nutritious and delicious.

KEY TERMS

Metabolism a set of reactions needed to keep the body functioning

Nutritionally dense foods foods that are a good source of several nutrients

Osteoporosis a disease where the bones become fragile and can break

Important nutrients needed by elderly people

Nutrient	Why it is needed	Sources
Energy from starchy, fibre-rich carbohydrates	Need energy but food should be in smaller portions	Wholemeal bread, pasta, rice, potatoes
Protein	Need protein for repair of tissues and body maintenance	Meat, fish, eggs, milk, cheese
Calcium	Needed for bone health and repair	Milk, cheese, green vegetables
Vitamin D	Works with calcium in bone formation	Sunlight, margarines
Iron	Needed for healthy blood, older people may get anaemic	Meat, green vegetables
Vitamin C	Helps iron absorption and wound healing	Fruit and vegetables
Thiamin	Needed for energy metabolism	Red meat, liver, milk, fortified breakfast cereals

Diet problems for older people

Problem	Diet changes
Bone problems	Make sure the diet is rich in calcium and phosphorus, and there is plenty of vitamin D from sunlight or food.
Anaemia	The diet should have good sources of iron and vitamin C.
Constipation	Make sure there is enough liquid and dietary fibre.
Weight regulation	Older people do not need to eat food in the same quantity that they did when they were younger.

If older people are frail and live alone, they may not prepare food for themselves, and so not eat a balanced diet. Some may be cooking for themselves for the first time and may need help with planning healthy meals. Older people may be on reduced incomes, so need to shop and plan nutritious meals carefully.

Meals on Wheels service

The Meals on Wheels service delivers a hot midday meal for people who are unable to cook for themselves and who have no one else who can help them. Local authorities usually organise the service for local people.

Meals on Wheels delivers good food to people's homes.

QUESTIONS

1. What nutrients are essential for the diet of elderly people?
2. What are the functions of two of these nutrients?
3. Describe a nutritious meal suitable for an older person. Give reasons for your choice.

Food for sport and exercise

Anyone taking part in regular exercise should choose food carefully, as this can improve performance and stamina. Keeping physically active and taking part in sport helps to burn off excess calories and maintain body weight. It also helps to reduce the risk of many diseases, such as heart disease. Regular exercise is important for good health and can include aerobics, working out in the gym, cycling, swimming, football, netball, dancing and walking.

Dietary requirements will vary according to the activity, but it is important to eat enough foods rich in starchy carbohydrate. We also need to drink plenty of fluid before, during and after exercise since fluid is lost in sweat. Water is the perfect drink to replace fluid loss.

Carbohydrates

Most people are encouraged to eat plenty of starchy, carbohydrate-rich foods – experts recommend that at least 50 per cent of food energy in the diet should come from carbohydrates. For sportspeople, carbohydrates should provide the main source of energy. Good carbohydrate-rich foods include rice, pasta, bread, cereals and potatoes.

Why do we need to increase our carbohydrates?

Carbohydrate-rich foods help to build up the **glycogen** reserves in the muscles that are needed to release energy during long, energetic activity. These glycogen supplies must be replaced after exercise to improve future training.

WEBSITES

Eatwell

KEY TERMS

Glycogen the form in which carbohydrate is stored in the liver

Supplements extra nutrients that can be eaten for health reasons

The carbohydrate in 100 grams of food	
Food 100 grams	Carbohydrate (grams)
Boiled rice	30
Boiled potatoes	20
Boiled pasta	26
White bread	50
Banana	19
Baked beans in tomato sauce	10
Cornflakes	85
Milk	5
Sugar	100

Protein

In the UK, most of us eat more protein than we need. For sport and exercise, there should be no need to increase the amount of foods rich in protein or to buy protein **supplements**. If we do eat too little, then we will not be able to keep up our exercise levels.

Tips on eating for sport and exercise

- Eat enough carbohydrate to keep going during exercise.
- Eat plenty of wholegrain breads and cereals, fruit and vegetables and moderate amounts of milk, yogurt and cheese, lean meat, fish, poultry, eggs, nuts and pulses.
- Eat enough food for the amount of exercise taken.
- Drink plenty of fluid – we need more than the six to eight glasses of water that are recommended a day.

When to eat for sport

For exercise that takes longer than one and a half hours, eat a high-energy snack such as a banana or some dried fruit beforehand or during exercise, or have some diluted fruit juice for energy.

For the first two hours after exercise, muscles refuel their glycogen stores twice as fast as normal. It is important to eat carbohydrate-containing foods as soon as possible after a workout or exercise session.

Supplements

A healthy, balanced diet should provide all the nutrients that are needed for sport and exercise, so food supplements should not be needed.

Tennis players like to eat bananas if they are playing a long match.

TO DO

- Plan a day's meals for someone taking part in a sport. Make sure the diet provides plenty of fluid and carbohydrate.

- Prepare a meal suitable for someone who has taken part in sport. Give reasons for your choice.

QUESTIONS

1. Why are carbohydrate-rich foods recommended for sportspeople?
2. Give four sources for carbohydrate-rich foods.
3. Why should we drink plenty of fluid during exercise?

Vegetarians 1

About one-quarter of the 6.5 billion people in the world eat a vegetarian diet.

A vegetarian does not eat any meat, poultry, game, fish, shellfish, crustacea or animal products, such as gelatin or animal fat such as suet. A vegetarian lives on a diet of grains, pulses, nuts, seeds, vegetables and fruits, with or without the use of dairy products and eggs. A strict vegetarian avoids products that come from animals, which include food, toiletries, clothes and household goods. Only cheeses marked suitable for vegetarians are eaten by strict vegetarians, as many cheeses contain animal rennet. Vegetarian cheeses are now widely available.

Vegetarians as a group have low rates of obesity, coronary heart disease and high blood pressure.

Types of vegetarian

- **Lacto ovo vegetarians** do not eat meat, poultry or fish, but will eat eggs and dairy products such as milk, yogurt, butter and cheese.
- **Lacto vegetarians** do not eat meat, poultry, fish or eggs, but will eat dairy products.
- **Vegans** do not eat any animal products, which include meat, poultry, fish, eggs, dairy products and bee products like honey.

Why do people choose a vegetarian diet?

There are many reasons why people choose to be vegetarians.

- **Religion** – vegetarianism is the dietary choice of several religions.
- **Health** – some people think that a vegetarian diet is healthier than one containing meat and meat products.
- **Animal welfare** – some people believe it is wrong to kill animals for food, or they object to intensive farming.
- **Taste** – some people do not like the taste of meat.
- **Environmental issues** – some people think that meat production is expensive compared with cereal and crop production, and that it is wasteful in resources and pollutes the environment.

WEBSITES

Vegetarian Society

Vegan Society

KEY TERMS

Lacto ovo vegetarians vegetarians who do not eat meat, but eat eggs and dairy products

Lacto vegetarians vegetarians who do not eat meat or eggs, but eat dairy products

Vegans vegetarians who do not eat any food from animals

Nutritional challenges

If vegetarians do not eat dairy products, they will need to find other sources of calcium, vitamin B2 and B12. Vegans may have low intakes of iron and zinc.

Good sources of nutrients include:

- protein from cereals, soya products, pulses and nuts and seeds
- wholegrain breads and breakfast cereals are fortified with nutrients
- dried fruits such as sultanas, figs, prunes and apricots contain iron.

By eating plenty of cereals, pulses, nuts and seeds, vegetarians have plenty of dietary fibre. This can mean their diet is bulky. For children, nutrient-dense food choices are important.

The Vegetarian Society logo.

Important nutrients for vegetarians

Nutrient	Why it is needed	Sources
Protein	Growth and repair	Milk, cheese, eggs, yogurt, soya milk, tofu, beans, lentils, peas, cereals, nuts and seeds
Iron	Healthy blood and forming haemoglobin; to prevent anaemia	Dried fruit (such as apricots), molasses, beans, lentils, egg yolks, wholegrain cereals and green vegetables
Vitamin C	Helps absorption of iron	Fresh, frozen and juice fruit and vegetables
Calcium	Healthy bones and teeth	Milk, cheese, soya, beans and chickpeas
Vitamin B12	Formation of red blood cells	Soya products, fortified breakfast cereals and bread, yeast extract
Vitamin D	Healthy bones and tissues	Sunlight, some margarines, soya milks
Selenium	Healthy immune system	Nuts such as Brazil nuts
Iodine	Needed to prevent thyroid problems	Iodised salt and kelp

QUESTIONS

1. List the different types of vegetarians.
2. Give two reasons why people might eat a vegetarian diet.
3. Name three nutrients that are important to vegetarians who do not eat animal products.

Vegetarians 2

Important nutrients in a vegetarian diet

Protein

Protein is needed for growth, and vegetarians need to make sure they are getting enough. Protein is made of amino acids, some of which are called **essential amino acids**, which have to be eaten as the body cannot make them. Meat, poultry, fish and eggs contain all the essential amino acids. Soya and quinoa are vegetarian sources of the complete mix of essential amino acids. Milk, cheese, eggs, yogurt, soya milk, tofu, beans, lentils, peas, cereals/grains, nuts, seeds, and mycoprotein such as Quorn are all good sources of protein for vegetarians. Some people believe that vegetarians should combine different types of protein foods at the same time such as beans on toast, rice with lentil dhal, humous and pitta bread.

The Vegan Society website on protein combining

Protein Combining – Is It Necessary?

Not really. Protein combining was based on the idea that complementary protein foods with different limiting amino acids, such as beans and grains, should be eaten at each meal in order to enhance the availability of amino acids.

This advice is now very old fashioned. Protein combining may reduce the amount of protein required to keep the body in positive protein balance but studies have indicated that this is neither necessary nor even always the case. Diets based solely on plant foods easily supply the recommended amounts of all the indispensable amino acids, and protein combining at each meal is unnecessary. Soya protein is actually equivalent in biological value to animal protein.

Iron

Studies show that vegetarians are no more likely to suffer from iron deficiency than meat eaters. Iron-rich vegetarian foods include dried fruit (such as apricots), molasses, beans, lentils, egg yolks, wholegrain cereals and green vegetables.

Vitamin C

Vitamin C increases the absorption of iron from plant foods and so it helps to have meals with iron and vitamin C together. Vitamin C is found in frozen, fresh or juiced fruit and vegetables.

Calcium

Vegetarians who eat eggs and dairy foods get enough calcium. Vegans may choose calcium-rich foods or soya drinks that have added calcium. Teenage girls who follow a vegetarian diet should make sure they eat enough calcium-rich foods to reduce the risk of osteoporosis in later life. Good sources of calcium for vegetarians include hard cheeses, soya products including tofu, fortified soya drinks, milk and yogurt, ice cream, white bread, beans, lentils and chickpeas.

Phytic acid, which is found in foods like spinach, blocks calcium absorption.

Vitamin B12

Vegetarians eating dairy products and eggs will get plenty of vitamin B12 in their diet. Foods from plant sources do not contain this vitamin, so fortified foods are the dietary source of vitamin B12 for vegans. Some soya drink products are also fortified with vitamin B12.

Selenium

Selenium is important for the immune system to function properly. Meat, fish and nuts are the best sources of selenium so, if you are a strict vegetarian, it is important to eat enough nuts, such as Brazil nuts.

Iodine

Iodine is provided by iodised salt in many countries, but in the UK the main source is dairy produce, because iodine is added to cattle feed. Iodine can be obtained from kelp, which is a type of seaweed. Low iodine intake can cause hypothyroidism, leading to tiredness, skin problems and raised cholesterol levels.

Vegetarian food symbols

Food producers have designed symbols to show that their food is suitable for vegetarians. The 'Suitable for vegetarians' logo is known as a 'voluntary claim'. The labelling information must not include anything that is false or likely to mislead, and whoever puts this information on the food label must be able to prove that it is true. Vegetarian food products cannot be made in the same place as products containing meat.

- The Vegetarian Society is a leading authority on the vegetarian diet.
- The Vegan Society has an approval system. Any vegan product must not contain eggs, milk or honey.

An example of a vegetarian symbol.

Food intolerance 1

Food intolerance or food allergy?

At least 20 per cent of the population believe they suffer from **food intolerances**, **allergies** or sensitivities. Some people have an acute, often violent reaction to specific foods such as nuts, gluten and strawberries – this is an allergic reaction.

A food intolerance happens when the body reacts to a certain food or food ingredient. True food intolerance affects less than 2 per cent of the population. Traces of the food in the diet can cause rashes, itching, diarrhoea, vomiting, swelling, breathing difficulties and even shock.

A food allergy is a type of intolerance that involves the immune system. This is usually because the body does not produce enough of the particular chemical or enzyme needed for digestion of that food.

Most intolerances are connected with these food groups:

- soya and soya proteins
- cow's milk
- wheat
- fish – cod, haddock, seafood and plaice
- nuts – almond, cashew nut, hazelnut and peanut (not strictly a nut).

How do you identify food intolerance?

If you react in an unusual way to some foods, you could be intolerant to them. If you suspect an allergy, see your general practitioner and get further tests. You should not alter your diet without medical advice.

KEY TERMS

Food intolerance when the body reacts to a certain food or food ingredient

Food allergy a type of intolerance that involves the immune system

Anaphylactic shock a potentially fatal condition caused by allergy to certain foods

Nutrition information

Ingredients: carrots (24%), Quark (17%), flour (14%), caster sugar, eggs, oil, orange juice, icing sugar, baking powder, mixed spice

Nutrition information	per 100g	per portion	GDA (women)	GDA (men)	GDA (5–10yr)	traffic light
Energy (kj)	1041.1 kj	1875.0 kj	22.3%	17.8%	24.8%	
Energy (kcal)	248.3 kcal	447.3 kcal	22.3%	17.8%	24.8%	
Protein	5.2 g	9.3 g	20.8%	17.0%	39.0%	
Carbohydrate	31.6 g	56.9 g	24.7%	18.9%	25.8%	
Fat	12.0g	21.7 g	31.1%	22.9%	31.1%	●

net weight: 1441 g   **allergens:** milk, gluten, wheat, egg

Food labels show that food contains allergens.

Foods that cause allergies and the symptoms

Type of intolerance or allergy	Foods to be avoided	Symptoms	What to do
Milk intolerance	Cow's milk	Wind, cramps, diarrhoea	Use other types of milk or soya milk.
Gluten intolerance	Wheat, rye, oats, barley	Children do not grow properly and there is weight loss	Avoid all foods made from wheat, barley, oats and rye.
Peanut allergy	Foods made with peanuts	Affects breathing and can cause anaphylactic shock	Avoid all foods made from peanuts.
Egg allergy	Foods made from eggs	Eczema and rash	Avoid all egg products.
Fish and shellfish allergy	All fish and shellfish	Nettle rash and anaphylactic shock	Avoid fish and shellfish.
Soya allergy	Soya products such as tofu	Eczema, asthma and diarrhoea	Avoid soya products.
Certain colourings and preservatives	Foods made with these colourings and preservatives	May cause hyperactivity in children	Avoid products with these colourings and preservatives.

Food Intolerance Data Bank

The UK Food Intolerance Data Bank started in 1987. Manufacturers submit data about their products and this data is used to produce a series of shopping guides that detail branded food products declared free from a particular additive or ingredient.

The fingerprick test

Are you suffering from irritable bowel syndrome, migraine, weight gain, dermatitis, eczema, psoriasis, arthritis or general tiredness? Food intolerance could be to blame. The fingerprick blood test measures any reaction when exposed to specific foods.

Anaphylaxis
This is a severe allergic reaction triggered by a wide range of foods. The most common foods that cause this reaction are peanuts and tree nuts. Tree nuts include almonds, Brazils, hazelnuts, cashews, walnuts, pecans and pistachios.

Anaphylactic shock is a potentially fatal condition and can develop in sensitive people within seconds or minutes of eating peanuts or other nuts.

QUESTIONS

1. What is a food intolerance?
2. What are the most common foods that cause food intolerance?
3. Name one type of food that causes an intolerance, then explain the foods that should be avoided and the symptoms.
4. What is anaphylactic shock?

Food intolerance 2

Coeliac disease

People with **coeliac disease** and those with gluten intolerance are unable to eat products made from wheat, barley, oats and rye, as they are sensitive to gluten (a protein found in these cereals).

In a healthy person, the lining of the small intestine is covered with fingerlike villi, which increase the surface area and help nutrient absorption. If people have coeliac disease, the lining of the small intestine is damaged by gluten. The villi flatten and the lining becomes inflamed. This damage prevents the absorption of nutrients so that weight loss and eventually malnutrition occur. Children who suffer from coeliac disease may not grow properly.

Gluten intolerance has a wide range of symptoms but if the disease is suspected, a doctor can carry out tests.

Foods to avoid

All foods containing wheat, barley, oats and rye must be removed from the diet – this means food such as bread, cereals, pasta, cakes, biscuits, pies and any foods made from wheat flour. Wheat flour contains about 12 per cent gluten.

Food labels must be checked carefully to see if they contain wheat products. Many ready-made foods such as gravies, custards, soups and sauces are thickened with wheat, rye, barley or other gluten-containing flour.

A label shows that the food is gluten free.

Gluten-free diet

Food manufacturers are very aware of this gluten intolerance and label their foods that are gluten-free. There are many gluten-free products designed to take the place of wheat, including:

- ready made gluten-free breads and pastas
- ranges of gluten-free flours
- gluten-free pasta
- cakes and muffin mixes.

People who need to avoid gluten can use flours made from:

- grains that are gluten free including millet, sorghum and rice
- flours made from beans and soya beans.

KEY TERMS

Coeliac disease gluten intolerance – foods with gluten cannot be eaten

The crossed grain symbol.

WEBSITES

Coeliac UK

Allergy UK

Gluten-free flours include rice, gram and other specialist flour.

Some of the foods products that people may be allergic to are:

- nuts and peanuts
- peanuts in sauces, cakes, desserts, groundnut oil and peanut flour
- nuts in sauces, desserts, crackers, bread, ice cream, marzipan, ground almonds and nut oils
- milk
- milk in yogurt, cream, cheese, butter, milk powders and foods glazed with milk
- soya as tofu or beancurd, soya flour and textured soya protein (TVP), in some ice cream, sauces, desserts, meat products and vegetarian products
- mustard, including liquid mustard, mustard powder and mustard seeds, in salad dressings, marinades, soups, sauces, curries and meat products
- lupin seeds and flour in some types of bread and pastries
- eggs in cakes, mousses, sauces, pasta, quiche, some meat products, mayonnaise and foods brushed with egg
- fish in some salad dressings, pizzas, relishes, fish sauce and some soya and Worcestershire sauces
- shellfish such as prawns, mussels, scampi, crab, oyster sauce and shrimp paste
- gluten in cereals such as wheat, rye and barley
- sesame in bread, breadsticks, tahini, humous, seeds and sesame oil
- celery including celery stalks, leaves and seeds and celeriac.

Allergens on the food label

The list of allergens shown on a food label includes:

| Peanuts | Nuts | Milk | Soya | Mustard | Eggs |
| Fish | Shellfish | Gluten | Sesame | Celery | |

> **INVESTIGATION**
>
> Investigate the nutritional details of a coeliac diet. Then plan a day's menu for someone who is allergic to nuts, peanuts and gluten.

Allergens on a food label.

> **QUESTIONS**
>
> 1. What foods should someone with coeliac disease avoid?
> 2. Name some foods that are gluten free.
> 3. Name two foods that should be avoided by people allergic to:
>   a) nuts and peanuts
>   b) soya
>   c) eggs.

School meals

History

The school meals service started in 1906, to provide meals for poorly nourished school children. The quality of meals varied over the years and the chef Jamie Oliver started a campaign for improvement. Today, meals served in schools must provide a specific **nutritional standard**.

New nutritional standards for school lunch

The new standards aim to:

- increase the intake of healthier foods
- restrict junk foods high in fat, sugar and salt
- improve the quality of food
- set minimum levels for the nutritional content of school meals.

The average school lunch must provide:

- no more than the maximum amount for fat, saturated fat, NME sugars and sodium
- at least the minimum amount of carbohydrate, protein, fibre, vitamin A and C, folate, calcium, iron and zinc.

WEBSITES

School Food Trust

KEY TERMS

Nutritional standards
standards that set limits for nutritional goals

Nutrient-based standards for school lunch			
Nutrient	**Minimum or maximum**	**Primary school**	**Secondary school**
Energy kcal		530	646
Carbohydrate	Min	50% of food energy	50% of food energy
Non-milk extrinsic (NME) sugars g	Max	15.5	18.9
Fat g	Max	20.6	25.1
Saturated fat g	Max	6.5	7.9
Protein g	Min	7.5	13.3
Fibre g	Min	4.2	5.2
Sodium mg	Max	499	714
Vitamin A µg	Max	175	245
Vitamin C mg	Min	10.5	14
Folate µg	Min	53	70
Calcium mg	Min	193	350
Iron mg	Min	3	5.2
Zinc mg	Min	2.5	3.3

Sources of energy

At least 50 per cent of energy should come from carbohydrate, with smaller amounts from fat (not more than 35 per cent) and protein. Students should choose starchy carbohydrates instead of food high in fat and sugar.

NME sugars

A diet high in NME sugars can lead to tooth decay. A survey found that school meals contain too many foods high in NME sugars. Fresh fruit should be offered instead of sugary puddings.

Fat

Too much fat can lead to excess energy intake and weight gain, so school meals should try to reduce the fat content and use lower-fat products. A diet high in saturated fat can lead to high cholesterol levels and increase the risk of heart disease, diabetes and some cancers. Products lower in saturated fats should be chosen and unsaturated fats used for cooking.

Salt

Salt is needed for nerve and muscle function and to maintain body fluid balance – but too much salt can cause high blood pressure. The salt content of school meals should be as low as possible, using herbs and spices to flavour food instead.

INVESTIGATION

Create your own two-course school meal and analyse it to see if it meets the school meal dietary requirements. Prepare and taste your meal. Get the views of others and try to improve and test again.

QUESTIONS

1. Name two improvements required by the new nutritional standards for school lunch.
2. Why should the amount of fat in the school lunch be limited?
3. How can the cook reduce the fat in a meal?
4. Why is it important that the salt content is low in a meal?
5. How can the cook lower the salt content of a meal?

Religion and food choices

Many religions have dietary rules that limit their food choices. The table on page 81 shows the food choices of different religious groups.

Religious laws concerning food

Christian

The Christian religion does not forbid eating any foods, but there is a tradition that fish is eaten on Fridays instead of meat.

Muslim

Food must be **halal**, which means that animals are slaughtered according to Islamic principles. Muslims do not eat pork, fish without scales and shellfish. Alcohol is forbidden.

Muslims avoid: pork and pork products including lard; gelatine from any animal source that is not halal; and any food or drink that has alcohol in it.

Jewish

Food must be **kosher** so the food meets Jewish dietary laws, or **kashrut**, which comes from the Hebrew word for 'fit' or 'proper'.

Kosher food must follow many rules, such as:

- pork and shellfish and some other animals are non-kosher and cannot be eaten
- meat and fowl must be slaughtered in a special way to be kosher
- meat and dairy products may not be made or eaten together.

Forbidden meat includes meat from pigs, eels, fish without scales and most shellfish. Meat must not be cooked or eaten in the same meal as dairy products and not cooked in butter. Separate cooking equipment is used for dairy products and meat.

Hindu

For Hindus, the cow is sacred and cannot be eaten. Not all Hindus avoid eating meat, but many Hindus are vegetarian. Alcohol is forbidden. Strict Hindu practitioners also abstain from garlic, onions, mushrooms, tea and coffee.

KEY TERMS

Halal food that is prepared according to Islamic principles

Kosher food that meets Jewish dietary laws and must follow special rules

Halal shop.

Kosher delivery van.

Buddhist

Many Buddhists are vegetarian as their religion preaches against killing. They can sometimes eat fish.

Sikh

Food restrictions are less strict than those for Muslims and Hindus. All meat except beef is allowed. Alcohol is forbidden.

Rastafarians

Some Rastafarians follow a vegetarian or vegan diet. For others, the restricted food depends on the individual.

Food choices	Muslim	Jew	Hindu	Buddhist	Sikh
Beef	halal	kosher	X	X	X
Pork	X	X	some	X	some
Other meat	halal	kosher	some	X	some
Non-scaly fish and shellfish	X	some	X	some	some

Food labelling

Halal

You can buy halal products from supermarkets and butchers that say they are halal. The Halal Food Authority is a UK-based organisation that outlines permissible standards in halal food for manufacturers.

Halal certification opens new markets for UK cheese group

Kosher food labels

Products that have been certified as kosher are labelled with kosher symbols. The symbols are printed on the food's package. Kosher symbols are registered trademarks of kosher certification organisations, and cannot be placed on a food label without the organisation's permission.

> ### QUESTIONS
>
> 1. What is meant by:
>   a) halal food
>   b) kosher food?
> 2. Name two foods that are forbidden for:
>   a) Muslims
>   b) Jews.
> 3. Explain why it is important to label halal and kosher food.

Welcome

The words in the questions

Look at the words in the questions. This will give clues on how much you need to write. There is also the mark at the end of the question that shows how many points you need to cover.

Questions that need short answers – which could be a few words

Give one example　　　　　　　*Name a nutrient*
Give three characteristics　　　*Name and describe*
Give three reasons for cooking food　*Name three good sources*
Give three ways　　　　　　　*Name two*
Give two different reasons　　　*Show one advantage and one disadvantage*
List two foods　　　　　　　　*What is the function?*

Questions that need longer answers – a sentence or paragraph

Define the term　　　　　　　*Explain what*
Describe with different reasons　*Explain the meaning of the following terms*
Discuss how　　　　　　　　　*Explain the reasons*
Discuss the nutritional value of　*Explain why*
Evaluate the effect of　　　　　*What is meant by?*

To cover questions on People and Food Needs you need to give your opinions as well as facts, and to use everyday experiences to help with answers.

Here is an example of a question for this section, and the factors to consider in writing a good answer.

Question

Explain what points need to be considered when feeding young children. (6 marks)

Answer

For this question, you need to list the points and explain why each is important.

Here are some expected answers.

- *Point* Provide balanced meals with a range of nutrients.
  Reason Ensures a healthy balanced diet.
- *Point* Keep food low in salt and sugar.
  Reason Helps prevent health problems later.

- *Point* Choose foods that are rich in calcium.
  Reason Needed for strong bones and teeth.
- *Point* Serve small portions of attractive food.
  Reason This encourages the child to eat and develop good eating habits.
- *Point* Choose a variety of foods, textures and colours.
  Reason This supplies the child with a range of nutrients.
- *Point* Encourage the child to eat family meals.
  Reason This helps them join in with family and form bonds.
- *Point* Make sure there are protein foods in the meal.
  Reason This helps the growth and development of the child.
- *Point* Avoid giving the child snacks and sugary drinks between meals.
  Reason This reduces the risk of dental caries.

Activity

Who are you feeding?

List three points that need to be considered when feeding and choosing food for:

	Points	Reasons
Pregnant woman		
Toddler		
Young child		
Teenager		
Busy family		
Elderly person		
Sportsperson		
Vegetarian		
Person with food intolerance		

Plan a meal for each person, and give your reasons for the choice, which should include identifying the nutrients and their function for each meal.

Meat and poultry

Meat

The range of meats to choose from includes beef, veal, lamb, pork and bacon.

Offal is the name for the internal organs of animals. Offal includes liver, heart, kidney.

Meat products include burgers and sausages, which can be made from beef, lamb and pork, meat pies and cook-chill meals.

Nutritional value of meat

Meat is made up of water, protein and fat. Lean meat is a good source of high-quality protein, iron and B group vitamins, especially B12.

Lowering the fat

Choose lower-fat versions of meat. Cut off excess fat from chops and steaks. You can buy lean and extra lean meat in supermarkets. This table shows the difference between the fat content of types of minced beef.

WEBSITES

Agriculture and Horticulture Development Board

Meat matters

KEY TERMS

Freedom Food and **Red Tractor** marks that show animals are reared with care

100 g meat	Traditional mince	Lean mince	Extra lean mince
Fat g	16.2	11.8	4.5
Saturated fat g	7.1	5.6	1.9

Cooking meat

Why is meat cooked?

- To kill bacteria and make meat safer to eat, which helps to prevent food poisoning.
- To make meat tender and easier to eat, and improve the texture.
- To improve the flavour and taste of meat.
- To improve the colour and appearance.
- To help the meat keep longer.

How does cooking affect the nutritional value of meat?	
Cooking changes	**Changes in nutrition**
Heating of meat.	Some B vitamins are destroyed by heat.
Juices escape from cooked meat.	Meat juices contain some minerals, vitamins and proteins.

Poultry

Poultry is the name given to chicken, turkey, duck and other birds. Due to intensive farming, chicken has become cheaper to buy, and is a versatile and nutritious food. In the UK:

- 95 per cent of chickens are reared indoors and a standard chicken is about 40 days old when it is slaughtered
- free-range chickens are allowed outside and reared in large sheds; they are 56 days old when they are slaughtered
- organic chickens are allowed to roam the fields and are given organic food to eat. They are 80 days old when they are slaughtered, but much more expensive to buy.

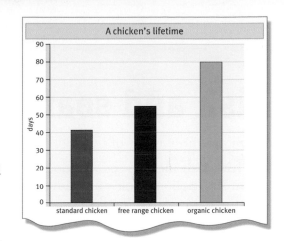

How long do farmed chickens live for?

Symbols on packaging to show that meat and poultry have met welfare standards		
Organisation	**Symbol**	**What they do**
Freedom Food		Freedom Food inspects farms to ensure they meet strict welfare standards covering all aspects of lives, including living conditions, handling and transport.
Red Tractor		A mark of quality that guarantees the food you are buying meets high standards of safety, hygiene, animal welfare and environmental protection.

Nutritional value of chicken

Chicken is lower in fat and higher in protein than red meat. It contains vitamin B6, B12 and the mineral selenium, which is an antioxidant and protects against heart disease.

100 g chicken	Energy kcal	Fat grams	Protein grams
Skinless chicken (raw)	106	1.1	24
Chicken with skin (raw)	201	4	19.1

Lowering the fat

To lower the fat in chicken, remove the skin. The table above compares the nutrition of chicken with and without the skin. However, the skin gives flavour to roasted chicken.

Storage of meat and poultry

Raw and cooked meat and poultry should be stored separately and kept cool in the refrigerator. Raw meat must be stored at the bottom of the refrigerator so that the juices do not drip onto other foods and contaminate them with bacteria. Poultry carries bacteria such as salmonella that can pass from one food to another and lead to food poisoning. Frozen poultry should be thoroughly thawed before cooking.

QUESTIONS

1. What is the nutritional value of meat and poultry?
2. How could you reduce the fat when choosing minced beef and chicken?
3. Give three reasons for cooking meat.
4. Why must meat and poultry be stored at the bottom of the refrigerator?

Fish and seafood

There are three types of seafood.

- **White fish** include cod, haddock, plaice, whiting, pollock, coley and dover sole.
- **Oily fish** include herring, mackerel, sardines, whitebait and tuna.
- **Shellfish** include:
  - molluscs – scallops, oysters, cockles, mussels, winkles.
  - crustacea – prawns, scampi, crabs, lobsters, shrimps
  - octopus, squid, cuttlefish.

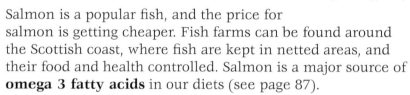

Different types of seafood.

We should eat at least two portions of fish a week, one of which should be oil rich.

Salmon is a popular fish, and the price for salmon is getting cheaper. Fish farms can be found around the Scottish coast, where fish are kept in netted areas, and their food and health controlled. Salmon is a major source of **omega 3 fatty acids** in our diets (see page 87).

Fish produced in fresh water include trout and carp, which is popular with eastern Europeans, especially at Christmas time.

KEY TERMS

Omega 3 fatty acids fatty acids found in oily fish that are important for a healthy heart

Nutrition in fish

Nutritional value of fish	
Nutrients	**Nutritional value**
Good source of protein	Needed for growth and repair
Essential fatty acids	Needed for cell membranes, cannot be made by body
Low in calories	Good for lower fat diets
Minerals – iron, zinc, iodine, selenium	Wide range of minerals
Vitamins A and D	Found in oily fish – important for growth and bones

Nutrition of 100 grams of fish									
	Energy kcal	Protein g	Fat g	Saturated fat g	Calcium mg	Iron mg	Zinc mg	Vitamin A	Vitamin D ug
Cod grilled	95	21	1.3	0.4	10	0.1	0.5	2	1
Mackerel grilled	239	21	17.3	3.5	12	1.2	0.7	48	8.8
Salmon grilled	215	24	13	2.5	25	0.5	0.7	16	7.1
Canned salmon	153	24	6.6	1.3	91	0.6	0.8	31	9.2

White fish have less than 5 per cent fat in their flesh; oily fish have 10–20 per cent fat in their flesh. Oily fish are a good source of **omega 3 fatty acids**, which are important for a healthy heart, lowering cholesterol levels and keeping our body healthy. Some fatty acids are made by the body, but some, like omega 3 fatty acids, cannot be made, and must be eaten. Oil-rich fish include salmon, trout, mackerel, sardines, and herring fresh, frozen or canned. Tuna is only counted as an oily fish if it is fresh or frozen.

Ways to buy fish and seafood

- Fresh from a fishmonger or supermarket – you have a choice of freshly caught fish.
- Frozen from the freezer of a supermarket – the fish is cut into portions and is frozen quickly after it is caught.
- Canned, such as canned salmon, mackerel and pilchards.
- Smoked, such as trout and salmon – smoking preserves and flavours the fish.
- Dried fish such as dried, salted cod – sold at room temperature and keeps for some time.
- Pickled, such as rollmops – preserved in vinegar which extends the shelf life.

Cooking fish

Fresh fish cooks very quickly, but if overcooked it becomes tough and dry. During cooking the muscles in the fish shrink and moisture is squeezed out.

The connective tissue in fish is called collagen and this changes into gelatine.

WEBSITES

Seafish Authority

QUESTIONS

1. What is the nutritional value of fish?
2. Why is it important to eat foods rich in omega 3 fatty acids?
3. Use the 'Nutrition of 100 grams of fish' chart. Which fish would you choose for:
   a) a low-calorie diet
   b) someone who needs foods rich in calcium and vitamins A and D?
4. What type of fish would you buy to use for:
   a) a sandwich filling
   b) a main meal
   c) a snack?
   Give reasons for each choice.

Eggs

In the UK we eat nearly 170 eggs each a year.

How are eggs farmed?

Eggs are farmed in three different ways: in laying cages (66 per cent), free range (27 per cent) and in barns (7 per cent).

- **Eggs from laying cages:** Hens are kept in laying cages, also known as battery farming. The hens are kept indoors, with controlled temperature, light and feed. This is the most popular and cheapest method of egg production.

- **Free-range eggs:** Free-range eggs come from hens that are allowed in open air runs and live in a hen house at night to protect them from foxes. Eggs are labelled free range on the packet. Organic eggs are free range and the hens live on organic land with an organic diet.

- **Barn eggs:** Here hens move about freely inside the barn, but the light and feed are controlled.

Eggs are sold in different sizes: small, medium, large and very large.

Free-range chickens.

Eggs in cooking

Eggs are a useful and versatile cooking ingredient. Without them, we couldn't make many sauces, omelettes, and most cakes, noodles and ice creams.

WEBSITES

British Egg

Functions and uses of eggs in cooking	
Functions	**Uses of eggs**
Binding	Bind or stick other ingredients together such as in beefburgers, fishcakes and croquettes.
Coating	Dip a fishcake in beaten egg then coat it with flour or breadcrumbs. The egg protects and coats the inside ingredients during frying.
Glazing	Glaze savoury pastry such as cheese straws and bread dough to make it golden when baked.
Thickening and setting	Thicken custards, flan, quiches, soups and sauces. The egg is a liquid food that contains protein, and this thickens with gentle heat.
Trapping air	Trap air when whisked or beaten. Used for meringues and cakes such as sponges. Also known as aerating and lightening.

Egg allergy

Egg allergy is most common in children under 12 months. Few children are allergic to egg after the age of six, though in some cases this allergy can persist into adult life, especially for people with a family history of the allergy.

Food safety

Eggs, like any protein rich food, need to be handled carefully. Here are some guidelines.

- Store eggs at a constant temperature below 20°C.
- Store away from strong smelling food – eggs are porous and absorb smells.
- Store away from raw meat – you may get cross-contamination from the meat.
- Wash your hands before and after handling eggs.
- Never use dirty, cracked, broken or washed eggs.
- Do not reuse left-over egg dishes.

Lion quality mark

Eggs displaying the Lion mark have been produced to the highest standard. Hens are tested for salmonella and hygiene is strictly controlled.

Nutrition in eggs

Eggs are a nutritious foods and good value for money. There is no recommended limit on how many eggs we should eat. Eggs offer:

- easily digestible protein needed for growth
- essential vitamins A,D, E and B groups – but no vitamin C
- minerals iron, phosphorus and zinc
- only 80–90 kcal an egg – they are low in saturated fat.

(!) Allergy advice | **May contain egg**

Allergy advice.

Lion quality mark.

TO DO

Eggs are a nutritious, good value food. Plan and prepare a meal that uses eggs as the main source of protein. Work out the cost of the meal for four people. Comment on your findings.

QUESTIONS

1. How are eggs farmed in the UK?
2. What is the Lion quality mark?
3. What functions and uses of eggs apply when making:
   a) fishcakes
   b) an egg flan
   c) a sponge cake?
4. What valuable nutrients do eggs provide?

Milk, cheese and yogurt

Milk

Pasteurisation makes milk safe and the heat kills harmful micro-organisms such as pathogenic bacteria, yeasts and moulds which may be present. Most milk is homogenised as well as **pasteurised**. **Homogenisation** breaks down the fat globules in milk, so there is no cream line on the top.

Different types of milk.

Types of milk

- **Whole milk** has about 4 per cent fat content.
- **Semi-skimmed milk** is the most popular type of milk in the UK with a fat content of 1.7 per cent. Many people prefer this when they want to lower the fat content in their diet.
- **Skimmed milk** has a fat content of between 0.1–0.3 per cent. Skimmed milk has nearly all the fat removed. It contains slightly more calcium than whole milk and less vitamin A.
- **1 per cent fat milk** is a new product; the milk contains less fat than semi-skimmed milk.

Other types of milk include dried milk, UHT (Ultra Heat Treated), evaporated and condensed milk. Organic milk comes from cows that have been grazed on pasture that has no chemical fertilisers, pesticides or agrochemicals used on it.

Nutrition in milk

Milk contains protein and is a good source of calcium, as well as the minerals zinc, phosphorus and magnesium. Milk contains the water-soluble vitamins Riboflavin, Thiamin and nicotinic acid. Vitamins A and D are found in whole milk.

Milk contains no dietary fibre or vitamin C. Most of the fat found in milk is saturated fat.

Cheese

Cheese is made by coagulating the protein in milk to make a curd, which is pressed to make a hard cheese such as Cheddar. Cheese that is suitable for vegetarians uses artificial rennet that does not come from animals. There are many varieties of cheese from different countries.

Nutrition in cheese

Cheese is a good source of protein and calcium. Cheese also contains vitamins A, B12 and D. Hard cheeses have the highest fat content and high energy values. Most cheese contains about 35 per cent fat. You can buy reduced-fat cheeses with less fat. Paneer is an Indian cheese that contains no rennet. It is made by adding an acid food, such as lemon juice, to hot milk.

Popular cheese dishes

- Margerita pizza
- Cheese quiche
- Matter paneer
- Macaroni cheese
- Cauliflower cheese
- Ploughman's lunch

Paneer is a cheese used in cooking.

Yogurt

Yogurt is made from warm milk, which has a culture of bacteria added. The yogurt thickens as the proteins coagulate. There are many types of yogurt, including low fat, very low fat and no fat. **Bioyogurt** has bacteria added, which give a mild taste and improve digestion.

Organic yogurt.

TO DO

Carry out some practical work to find out how to encourage people to use more milk, milk products and cheeses in their cooking. Test and taste some recipes and work out the cost and nutritional value of the recipes. Write a short evaluation of your work.

QUESTIONS

1. Give three reasons why people decide to use different types of milk.
2. Copy and complete the table below to show different nutrients found in milk, and give their use in the body. The first one has been done for you.

Nutrients in milk	Use in the body
Protein	Needed for growth and repair of body tissues. Excess is used as a source of energy.

3. Give three reasons why cheese is a nutritious food.
4. List two dishes that can be made from cheese.
5. What is bioyogurt?

New protein: Quorn™ and novel foods

Soya protein

Soya protein is made from soya beans and is used in many food products. Soya beans are a high-quality protein, as soya contains most of the essential amino acids.

Soya protein products include soya flakes, soya meal and textured protein products. These are made from soya flour, with water and additives added to form a dough, which is extruded (stretched) to create a meat-like structure to products.

In 1970, a meat-like soya product was created and given the trade name TVP, or textured vegetable protein. This product can be made into different shapes and sizes, and even into products that look like ham, beef and poultry but which are low in fat. Granose soya mince is made from 100 per cent dried soya mince and has no artificial colours or flavours. You need to add water to make it ready to cook.

Tofu

Tofu is soya bean curd, made by setting soya milk with calcium sulphate. Silken tofu is soft and creamy, while firm tofu can be cut into chunks and used in stir-fries. Tofu is a good source of protein and has been used in Chinese and Far eastern cooking for hundreds of years.

Mycoprotein: Quorn™

Quorn™ is a registered trademark for a mycoprotein, which is a fungal protein. Quorn™ can be made into many varieties of food with good flavour and texture, and a good nutritional profile. It is high in protein and fibre, and low in total fat and saturated fat. The protein has a high biological value, which means it is close to the mix of amino acids that meet our dietary needs. Quorn™ contains most of the B vitamins, except B12.

> ### KEY TERMS
>
> **Soya protein** protein from soya beans made into textured vegetable protein (TVP) and soya mince
>
> **Quorn™** a mycoprotein that comes in many shapes and sizes
>
> **Novel foods** foods invented for us to eat, rather than grown or farmed naturally
>
> **Functional foods** foods that claim to have health-promoting properties

Soya chunks are textured vegetable protein.

Soya products.

To make Quorn™, the mycoprotein is fermented, mixed with egg white and flavours, then processed into different textures.

Quorn™ products

There is a huge range of Quorn™ products for sale. These include mince and pieces, which can be used like meat in cooked dishes. There are also shaped products such as burgers, fillets and sausages, which can be cooked on their own as meals.

Novel foods

Novel Foods are foods that have been invented for us to eat. They have to pass the test of the Advisory Committee on Novel Foods and Processes (ACNFP). Quorn™ was the first novel food to be accepted by the ACNFP.

Functional foods claim to have a health-promoting or disease-preventing property. The range of functional foods includes soft drinks, breakfast cereals, and baby foods. Probiotic yogurt, which contains probiotic bacteria, which may help to maintain the natural balance of your digestive system, is a functional food. Spreads that lower your cholesterol levels also promote health.

WEBSITES

Quorn™

FACT

Quorn™ was invented in 1985 as a new protein food.

Products that imitate meat such as Quorn™ and TVP are called meat analogues or meat substitutes.

INVESTIGATION

Use the Internet to research the range of Quorn™ products for sale. Find the cost and the nutritional value of the products. Write a report to show why sales of these products are increasing.

TO DO

Compare the cooking properties of minced beef with soya mince and Quorn™ mince. You can make three identical dishes like cottage pie, bolognese or chilli con carne, then taste and compare the results for flavour and cost. Carry out a nutritional analysis of each dish. Write a report on your findings.

QUESTIONS

1. How are soya beans used to make soya mince?
2. What is Quorn™ and how is it made?
3. What are:
   a) novel foods
   b) functional foods?
   Give examples.
4. Why do you think people want to eat soya mince and Quorn™?

Fruits and vegetables

Fruit and vegetables come in many shapes, sizes and flavours – just think of the selection in your local shop. They are among the best sources of nutrition for almost everyone. For a healthy diet, we should eat five portions of fruit and vegetables a day. These portions can be fresh, frozen, dried fruit and fruit juice or canned vegetables, but do not include potatoes. Our consumption of vegetables is the lowest in Europe.

Nutritional values

- Fruit and vegetables are low in fat (except for avocado pears). Fruit and vegetables are good sources of dietary fibre.
- Citrus fruit such as oranges, lemons, and blackcurrants are rich sources of vitamin C
- Yellow, red and orange fruit and vegetables supply the antioxidant pigment betacarotene, which is a form of vitamin A.
- Antioxidant vitamins A, C and E protect against certain diseases such as cancer.

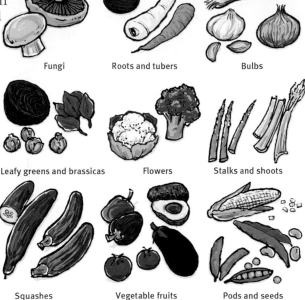

Fungi   Roots and tubers   Bulbs

Leafy greens and brassicas   Flowers   Stalks and shoots

Squashes   Vegetable fruits   Pods and seeds

Vegetables should be cooked as quickly as possible to save nutrients.

What changes take place in cooking?

- **Loss of Vitamin C:** When fruit and vegetables are chopped and prepared, the cell walls are cut, which lets the enzymes destroy the vitamin C. Vitamin C is water-soluble, so it will leak out into cooking water. Heat and time will destroy vitamin C.
- **Browning:** When some fruit is cut, such as apples, pears and bananas, the surface can go brown. The enzymes in the fruit react with the oxygen in the air and change – a process called enzymic browning. Add an acid such as lemon juice to prevent this change.

Fruit and vegetables to choose		
Types to choose	**Nutrition**	**Healthy eating advice**
Fresh, frozen and canned fruit and vegetables and dried fruit. A glass of fruit juice. Beans and pulses can be eaten as part of this group.	vitamin C, carotenes, folates, fibre and some carbohydrate.	Eat a wide variety of fruit and vegetables. Try to avoid: • adding fat and rich sauces to vegetables • adding sugar and syrupy dressings to fruit (e.g. adding chocolate sauce to banana).

- **Other changes:** With heat, the cell walls of fruit and vegetables soften. Water leaks out. The more they are cooked, the softer they get. Too much cooking can make vegetables unpleasant to eat.

Preserving fruit and vegetables

Most fruit and vegetables do not stay fresh for long, but there are different ways to preserve them to increase their shelf life.

- **Freezing:** Peas are one of the most popular frozen vegetables. They are often better quality than fresh peas as they are picked and frozen immediately. Few nutrients are lost in freezing. Other frozen vegetables include beans, carrots and mixed vegetables.
- **Canning:** Fruit and vegetables are canned, heated and sealed at high temperatures, which softens them. Some vitamin C is lost in canning.
- **Drying:** Moisture is removed during drying so that the food cannot deteriorate. Sultanas, prunes and apricots are examples of dried fruits.
- **Jams and chutneys:** Fruit is boiled with plenty of sugar to make jam, and vegetables are cooked in vinegar and sugar to make chutney. These products are generally high in sugar.

Ways to save vitamins

- Buy fruit and vegetables in season, when they are fresh.
- Buy good-quality fruit and vegetables that are not bruised and damaged, as enzymes change the nutritional value.
- Store in a cool, dark place for a short time – sunlight will make them deteriorate.
- Unpeeled vegetables contain more dietary fibre, so peel vegetables thinly.
- Cook vegetables quickly in a little water. Steaming or microwaving are quick methods and lose fewer minerals and vitamins.
- Prepare fruit and vegetables just before you need them – vitamin C is destroyed by heat and time.
- Cook them immediately after preparing them.
- Eat raw fruit and vegetables, as this saves cooking losses.
- Do not leave vegetables to stand in water, as nutrients leak out and are lost.
- Do not chop fruit and vegetables into too small pieces, as this exposes more of the surface and nutrients are lost.
- Do not keep cooked vegetables warm for too long, as the vitamins are lost.

Fruit and vegetables

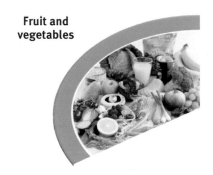

Fruit and vegetables on the eatwell plate.

Beans and pulses, nuts and seeds

Pulses are seeds that include beans, lentils and peas. They are a low-fat source of protein, fibre, vitamins and minerals, and count as a portion of fruit and vegetables.

Different kinds of pulses.

Beans and pulses

The bean and pulse group includes butter beans, pinto beans, red and black kidney beans, lentils, peas and soya beans. India is the world's largest producer of pulses.

Nutrition of pulses

Pulses contain more protein than any other vegetable and are a good source of dietary fibre. They contain carbohydrates, B group vitamins and some iron. Beans and pulses are popular foods for vegetarians as they contain protein needed for growth and repair.

Cooking beans

Beans and pulses are often dried and need soaking in water before cooking. Some dried beans, including kidney beans, contain toxins in their outer skins and must be soaked for twelve hours and then boiled for fifteen minutes to destroy these toxins. Canned beans have been through this process, so are safe to use straight from the can.

Popular pulses

- **Peas** are rich in protein, carbohydrate and fibre and low in fat, a good source of vitamin A, vitamin C, folate, thiamin (B1), iron and phosphorus. Frozen peas are as nutritious as fresh peas. The UK is the largest producer of peas for freezing in Europe.
- **Baked beans** are a popular, nutritious food and a good source of inexpensive protein.
- **Chickpeas** are used for hummus, a dish of ground chickpeas, tahini paste, oil and garlic.
- **Chana dhal**, a lentil similar to a chickpea, is used to make gram flour. This flour is used in Asian cooking, and is a gluten-free alternative to ordinary flour.
- **Lentils** – red, green, brown, black and yellow – are used a lot in Indian cooking, such as in spicy dhal. Lentils are a good source of protein and iron.

WEBSITES

Birds Eye

KEY TERMS

Pulses include beans and lentils, and are the seeds of plants called legumes

Legume an upright or climbing bean or pea plant

Frozen peas are a good source of protein and vitamin C.

- **Soya beans** are usually made into soya products, such as soya milk, tofu, TVP and soya sauce. They are a complete form of protein, which means they contain all the essential amino acids, so are a good replacement for animal protein foods. They are often made into cooking oil.

Nutrition for 100 grams of pulses and beans				
	Energy kcal	Protein g	Carbohydrate g	Fibre g
Chickpeas, canned	115	7.2	16	4.1
Lentils, boiled	100	7.6	17.5	1.9
Peas, frozen	62	4.9	9	4.5
Soya beans, frozen	145	14	4.8	6

Many beans and seeds can be sprouted to eat in salads and are a good source of vitamin C. Mung beans are sprouted to become bean sprouts, popular in Chinese stir-fries.

Nuts and seeds

Nuts

Nuts are nutritious, providing protein and vitamins, such as A and E, the minerals phosphorous and potassium, and fibre. Nuts are high in carbohydrate and fats, so do not eat too many of them.

Peanuts are **legumes,** but many people think they are nuts. They are high in protein and contain 40–50 per cent oil, which is made into cooking oil and margarines. Whole peanuts are eaten raw, or roasted and made into peanut butter. Peanuts are cheap, so they are mixed with foods to bring down the cost.

Seeds

Seeds provide protein. They can be added to salads, breads and biscuits to give texture and flavour, as well as adding extra fibre. Popular seeds include sunflower, pumpkin and sesame.

INVESTIGATION

Prepare a veggie burger using different pulses and beans. Make and taste it and find the nutritional value and cost for 100 grams. Compare this with a minced beef burger. Which do you prefer and why?

Seeds are used to give texture and flavour to bread, biscuits and salads.

QUESTIONS

1. List three important nutrients found in pulses and give the function of each.
2. Explain why pulses are an important part of the diet for so many people around the world.
3. What is the nutritional value of nuts?
4. Give an example each of dishes that use:
   a) lentils
   b) beans
   c) nuts
   d) seeds.

Chapter 3

Potatoes

Potatoes are an important source of starch in our diet and, because we eat so many of them, they are a good source of vitamin C. Potatoes are a **staple food** in the UK. Staple foods make up the main part of a traditional diet and are often rich sources of starch. Rice, wheat, cassava and yams are staple foods in different parts of the world. Potatoes are cheap, nutritious and filling, and can be cooked in many ways.

Types of potato

New potatoes are available in the late spring; they must be eaten soon after purchase. Main crop potatoes are harvested from September and can be kept for many months if properly stored. You can choose a variety of potato to suit your cooking needs.

Potatoes are both versatile and nutritious.

Nutrition in potatoes

- 100 g of boiled potatoes contains just 72 calories.
- Eat a whole jacket potato and get 2.7 g of fibre.
- 100 g of oven chips contains twice as much vitamin C as an apple. Rice and pasta contain no vitamin C at all.
- Potatoes contain 33 times more vitamin B6 than pasta, and 18 times more thiamin than rice or pasta.
- Boiled potatoes give you one-third more fibre than boiled rice.

Cooking methods

Potatoes can be boiled, baked, roasted, microwave, fried or deep-fried to make chips.

KEY TERMS

Staple foods foods that make up the main part of a traditional diet, and are usually starch

WEBSITES

Potato Council

Potatoes				
Boiling	**Baking**	**Roasting**	**Microwave**	**Chips**
Boiling – water soluble vitamins lost	Baking – keep skins on for fibre	Roasting – absorb fat	Microwaving – not many nutrients lost	Chips – absorb fat

Nutrition for cooking potatoes.

- **Boiling:** Peel potatoes thinly to avoid waste and save nutrients stored under the skin. Cook in enough water to cover, so that fewer minerals and vitamins are lost in the water. Use potato water for stock and soups. Rapid cooking reduces nutrient losses.
- **Baking:** Potatoes baked in their skins lose 20–40 per cent of their vitamin C content. Small potatoes bake more quickly than large ones and keep more of their vitamin C.
- **Roasting:** When potatoes are roasted with meat or in fat, they absorb a proportion of the fat and their energy value increases. About 60–70 per cent of their vitamin C is kept.
- **Microwaving:** This is a good way to cook a potato in a hurry, and few nutrients are lost. Microwaves make water molecules in food vibrate, which produces heat and cooks the potato.
- **Chipping:** Chips fried for 15 minutes keep 60–70 per cent of their vitamin C. Calorific value increases, as they absorb the fat in which they are fried. Thick-cut chips absorb less fat than thin-cut chips.

Changes in cooking

During cooking, the starch grains absorb water and they swell and become soft.

The starch gelatinises during cooking. Because of this, potatoes can be used to thicken stews and soups. This type of starch does not break down when frozen, so potato products freeze well. If the potato is fried or roasted, it absorbs fat.

FACT

One out of every four British potatoes is made into chips. Ten per cent of the entire British potato crop is needed to supply all the fish and chip shops.

QUESTIONS

1. Name three nutrients found in a potato.
2. What happens when a potato is cooked?
3. Copy and complete the table to show the advantages and disadvantages of each method of cooking for potatoes.

	Advantages	Disadvantages
Boiling		
Baking		
Roasting		
Microwaving		
Chipping		

Cereals

Cereals are plant seeds. They are a valuable source of starch, which we use for food energy. Cereals provide protein for growth and the wholegrain is a good source of fibre, which helps our digestive system. Cereals are called a staple food because they form the main part of the diet for many people of the world. Maize, rice and wheat are the main cereals grown.

This pie chart shows the main cereal crops of the world.

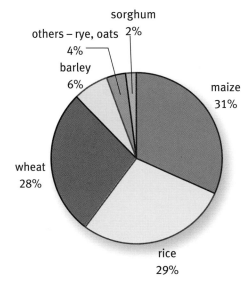

sorghum 2%

others – rye, oats 4%

barley 6%

maize 31%

wheat 28%

rice 29%

World cereal crops.

Cereals are staple foods – rice, wheat and maize.

All cereal grains are similar in structure. The endosperm is the main part which contains starch and sugar. Bran is the outer coating, and contains fibre and B vitamins. The wheatgerm is where the new plant grows, and contains fat and B vitamins.

What do we use cereals for?

Many breakfast cereals are fortified with vitamins and minerals, so are important sources of iron, folic acid and vitamins B and D. Breakfast cereals are also a good source of fibre.

Eating more wholegrain cereals and slowly absorbed starches is linked with a reduced risk of coronary heart disease, which has major health benefits for the UK population.

Rice is a starchy accompaniment to many meals. It contains some dietary fibre food a little protein.

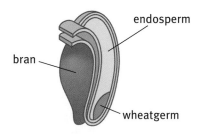

endosperm

bran

wheatgerm

Grain of wheat.

WEBSITES

Flour Advisory Bureau

Uses of cereals and their nutrition values

Wheat	Maize	Rice	Oats	Rye
Milled into flour, made into bread, pasta, couscous, pastry, biscuits, breakfast cereals	Milled into cornflour, made into breakfast cereal, polenta	Milled into rice flour, made into breakfast cereals	Used for porridge, flapjacks, bread	Milled into flour and used for bread

Nutrition in 100 grams of cereals

White flour	Cornflour	Rice flour	Porridge oats	Rye flour
10 g protein	0.6 g protein	0.6 g protein	12 g protein	8 g protein
80 g carbohydrate	92 g carbohydrate	80 g carbohydrate	58 g carbohydrate	76 g carbohydrate
3.1 g fibre	0.1 g fibre	4 g fibre	9 g fibre	12 g fibre

Flour

White flour	Wholemeal flour	Stoneground flour	Strong flour – for bread
White endosperm – about 72% of wheat grain	80–90% of grain used	100% flour and wholegrain	Made from hard wheat with higher protein content
Used for thickening sauces, pastry and bread-making, cakes and biscuits	More nutritious than white flour and used in bread and pastries	Good flavour and used for breads and pastries	Used for breadmaking

Pasta

Italian pasta is made from durum wheat, a variety of strong wheat. Pasta is made by mixing together flour and water or egg to make a paste and extruded through holes to make different shapes, such as spaghetti, fusilli or lasagne.

Pasta is a good source of carbohydrate, and contains some protein, dietary fibre, B vitamins, potassium and iron. Wholewheat pasta provides more dietary fibre than white.

Different types of flour.

QUESTIONS

1. What are the main nutrients found in cereals?
2. Maize, wheat and rice are the most popular cereals that we eat. Make a list of three foods made from each of these cereals.
3. Which of the cereals contains the most:
   a) protein
   b) carbohydrate
   c) fibre?

Bread

Bread is an important food for the UK. It is a good source of carbohydrate, protein, B group vitamins, dietary fibre and calcium and iron.

There are many kinds of bread on sale from all over the world. In the UK, most of the bread we eat is white, brown or wholemeal bread made from wheat flour.

- **White bread** is made from white flour, which is fortified with added vitamins, iron and calcium.
- **Brown bread** is made from flour, with some bran and wheatgerm removed.
- **Wholemeal bread** is made from wholemeal flour, it contains more fibre than white.

There are many kinds of bread flour too.

- Granary flour for colour, texture and flavour.
- Malted wheat flour for flavour and texture.
- Strong white flour for well-risen bread.
- Rye flour for a dense, darker bread.
- Wholemeal flour for a dark brown, nutty bread.
- Spelt flour can be used in place of wheat flour.

How bread is made

Bread is made from strong wheat flour, liquid and a raising agent such as yeast.

To make the bread, ferment the yeast with sugar and water, and mix into the flour and salt. Knead, prove and shape, then bake until the outside is crisp.

INVESTIGATION

Find out about the range of breads for sale and any special nutritional claims such as added fibre. Present a report on your findings.

WEBSITES

Federation of Bakers

Different types of bread.

Ingredient	Function
Strong flour – wheat	Strong flour is high in gluten. Gluten forms the structure, is able to stretch, is strong and smooth. It forms the network that is stretched by the carbon dioxide gas. The gluten proteins coagulate and become solid when cooked, forming a stable, risen product. The starch in the flour is converted to dextrin, which caramelises to give the bread crust its colour.
Yeast	Yeast ferments with sugar, flour and water. It produces carbon dioxide gas, which is a raising agent. The gas pushes up the structure and makes the bread rise.
Water	Water binds the dry ingredients together, works with the gluten to stretch the dough, gives lightness and acts as a raising agent. The water helps the yeast to ferment.
Salt	Salt works with the gluten and provides flavour.

Baking bread in a bakery

A computer-controlled system manages the process of bread-making in a bakery. This makes sure that the bread is the same texture, taste and weight every time.

Bakeries often work 24 hours a day, seven days a week.

Flour is stored before it is sifted. Flour and water are measured and mixed to a dough in a high-speed machine. The dough is divided into loaves, shaped and dropped into tins. The loaves move to a proving area to increase in size.

The tins pass into a hot oven for baking. The loaves cool, and pass through a metal detector. For sliced loaves, sharp blades slice the loaf according to thickness. The bread is bagged, labelled and loaded onto vans for delivery to supermarkets and shops.

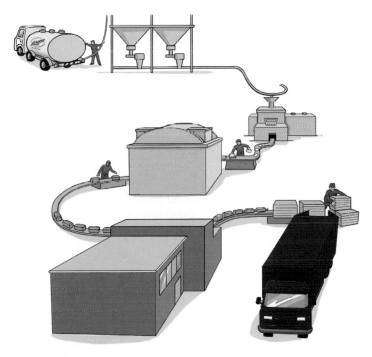

Stages in making bread.

QUESTIONS

1. What is the nutritional value of bread?
2. Describe in steps how bread is made.
3. What is the function of the following ingredients in bread: flour, yeast, water and salt?
4. How does a commercial bakery control the quality of bread?

Additives

Many packaged foods contain additives. In the UK, there are more than 300 listed additives and more than 3,000 flavourings. Additives are used to help food keep safe longer, to stop oils and fats from going rancid and to add colour. If additives were not used, we would have fewer food choices since food would not last as long, and many lower-fat products would not be available.

There are three groups of additives:

- **natural** – made from natural products, such as paprika and beetroot juice
- **nature identical** – made to the same chemical formula as those extracted from natural products – for example, caramel used for colouring
- **artificial** – made entirely from chemicals – for example, saccharin used to sweeten foods.

The ingredient list on a food label shows if any additives are used in the product.

Are additives safe?

Some additives have been used for many years. Potassium nitrate (E251) has been used for curing bacon and ham, and pectin (E440a) in jam-making. Some people are sensitive to certain additives and need to avoid them. Tartrazine (E102), used to colour soft drinks, has been linked to food allergies.

Additives used in the UK have been strictly tested. An 'E-number' shows that the additive has been accepted as safe by the countries of the European Union.

Types of additive

- **Preservatives** help food to keep longer so that food can be transported and the storage time is increased. Preservatives are used in baked goods, soft drinks, bacon and ham, and fruit juices.
- **Antioxidants** prolong shelf life, stop fatty food from going rancid and protect fat-soluble vitamins from combining with oxygen. Antioxidants are used in dried soups, cheese spreads and sausages. Ascorbic acid (vitamin C) is a natural antioxidant that is found in fruit and prevents other fruit going brown. This is why lemon juice is added to peeled apples.

WEBSITES

Food Standards Agency

Understanding Food Additives

KEY TERMS

E-number a number showing that the additive has been accepted as safe by the countries of the European Union

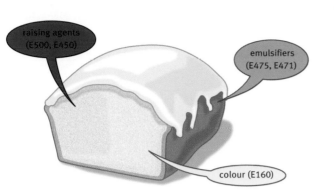

How can additives help the shelf-life of this cake?

What flavouring and preservatives are used in hot dogs? Why are they used?

- **Colours** are added to food to make it look more attractive and to replace the colour that might be lost during processing. During canning, peas and strawberries both turn brown, so colours can make them look more attractive. Caramel (E150) is the most popular colouring used for gravy powder, soft drinks and sauces.

- **Emulsifiers and stabilisers** allow fats and oils to mix with water to make low-fat spreads and salad dressings. They give food a smooth and creamy texture, and improve the shelf life of baked goods. Lecithin, found in eggs, is a natural emulsifier used in mayonnaise and in low-fat spreads.

- **Intense sweeteners** (artificial sweeteners) such as saccharin and aspartame are many times sweeter than sugar, and only a little is needed. Intense sweeteners help people to eat less sugar since they are low in calories. They are used for low-calorie drinks and reduced-sugar products.

- **Flavourings** add flavours to foods, such as vanilla in ice cream. A flavour is natural, nature identical or artificial. Monosodium glutamate (MSG) is a flavour enhancer that has no flavour of its own, but intensifies the flavours of other foods. A small number of people may be allergic to monosodium glutamate.

INVESTIGATION

Investigate how additives are used in food products. Look at food labels and the Internet for lists of ingredients. Keep a record of your findings. Comment on your results.

QUESTIONS

1. What is an E-number?
2. Give three reasons why additives are used in food products.
3. What are your views on food additives? Give the case for and against using additives in food products.

Convenience food

Convenience foods have been prepared to make them easier to use. They are packaged in cans, bottles, cartons and bags, and sold as dried, frozen and chilled food products.

Here are some examples of convenience foods.

- **Canned food** – soup, baked beans, dhal, curry sauce, coconut milk.
- **Cartons of food** – soups, sauces, drinks.
- **Dried food** – dried soup, pots of noodles, rice dishes.
- **Dried food mixes** – cake mix, pancake mix, custard, bread mix.
- **Frozen food** – ready meals, battered fish, beefburgers, cheesecake.
- **Chilled food** – ready meals, garlic bread, desserts.

Convenience food is available in a range of packaging.

Some people are concerned about the increased use of convenience foods. The food is portion-controlled, needs special packaging, and must be stored for some time, so it loses its freshness and is not as nutritious as fresh food. It may have high levels of salt and preservatives which means it can be stored for longer. However, convenience food saves preparation time, a meal is ready to heat up when needed, and you can buy portions of food to suit your needs.

TV dinners and ready meals

TV dinners, where the whole meal is ready to heat and eat, were invented in the 1950s. Today there is a huge range of complete meals that you can buy from supermarkets, such as an Indian Chicken Tikka Meal Box For One, which contains chicken tikka masala, pilau rice, mini naan bread and two onion bhaji.

Cook-chill food

Cook-chill foods include ready meals and desserts. The food is chilled quickly after cooking – within one and a half hours to just above 0°C – to prevent bacteria from multiplying. Cook-chill foods are distributed and stored at temperatures between 0°C and 8°C, and should be used by the 'use by' date on the packaging. The food must be reheated to reach 72°C at the centre and eaten within two

> **KEY TERMS**
>
> **Convenience food** food that is ready-prepared to make it easy to cook and eat
>
> **Cook-chill food** food that is cooked then chilled to very low temperatures

hours of reheating. Cook-chill foods must only be reheated once.

Why are cook-chill meals becoming so popular?

- Cook-chill meals are widely advertised on TV and in magazines.
- Food is ready to eat, convenient and widely available.
- Lifestyles are changing and people have less time to cook.
- You do not need to buy a range of ingredients to make the meal, so they can be cheaper.
- You do not need any cooking skills.
- There is little wastage and you do not need to shop for ingredients.
- The meal can meet your price range.
- There is a wide selection of foods from around the world.
- Meals can meet the needs of different people – vegetarians, children and fussy eaters.
- There is plenty of information on the label to tell you the nutrition, ingredients, how to cook, and allergens.

Who might find cook-chill meals value for money?

- Useful for people living and cooking for themselves, as it gives variety of meals.
- Elderly people who cannot easily shop or cook.
- Families who have people with special dietary needs or fussy eaters, when individual meals can be bought.
- People who are busy and work shifts and want a quick meal when they come home.

Disadvantages of cook-chill meals

- The food is not freshly prepared.
- You cannot be sure of the quality of ingredients.
- You are not using any cooking skills.
- The meals may be expensive.
- The meals might be higher in salt and fat than ones cooked yourself.
- They may contain preservatives and flavourings to help them keep longer.

INVESTIGATION

Compare the cost and nutrition of a cook-chill meal with making the same meal from scratch (buying, preparing and cooking all the different parts of the meal).

WEBSITES

Canned Food UK

Iceland

Sainsbury's

Tesco

QUESTIONS

1. Give three examples of useful convenience foods for:
   a) an older person living alone
   b) a student
   c) a busy family.
   In each case, give two reasons for your choice.

2. What are the disadvantages of eating a diet with lots of convenience foods?

3. Give two examples of cook-chill meals. Give three reasons why people choose these foods.

Cooking methods 1

Why do we cook food?

Cooking makes food tastier, more attractive and easier to eat. Raw potatoes cannot be eaten, but they can be boiled, roasted and fried. Cooking makes food safer to eat, as harmful bacteria are killed if heated to a high enough temperature for a long enough time. Cooked food keeps longer than fresh food, as yeasts, moulds and bacteria are killed with heat. Cooking also improves the flavour of many foods such as cooking lentils, spices and garlic together to make dhal – a lentil curry.

How is food cooked?

The three ways heat energy can pass to food are convection, conduction and radiation.

Convection

Heat travels round liquids and air by **convection** currents. Ovens are heated by convection currents. The hot air rises and the cool air falls, which is why a conventional oven is hotter at the top. Cooking methods that use convection currents include boiling food in a saucepan and baking cakes in an oven.

Conduction

Heat is **conducted** from molecule to molecule in solids or liquids. Heat is conducted round the metal in pans and through a joint of meat as it roasts. Metals are good conductors. They are used for saucepans and baking trays. Poor conductors of heat include wood and plastic. Wooden spoons are used to stir things as they do not get hot. Copper is a good conductor of heat and is sometimes used on the base of pans to speed up heat transfer.

Radiation

Heat travels in waves or rays that heat up food. Food that is grilled or toasted is cooked by **radiation**. The direct infrared rays heat the food when they are absorbed.

> ## KEY TERMS
>
> **Convection** when heat travels round liquids and air by convection currents
>
> **Conduction** when heat is conducted from molecule to molecule in solids or liquids
>
> **Radiation** when heat travels in waves or rays

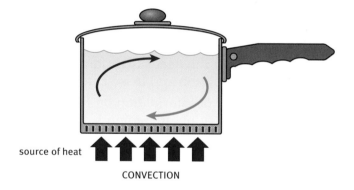

source of heat

CONVECTION

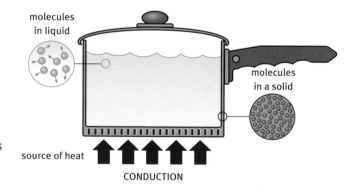

molecules in liquid

molecules in a solid

source of heat

CONDUCTION

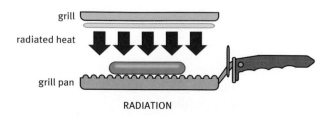

grill

radiated heat

grill pan

RADIATION

Methods of cooking – convection, conduction, radiation.

Most food is cooked by a combination of methods of heat transfer. A baked potato is cooked in an oven by convection currents carrying the heat around the oven to the potato. The heat is then conducted through the potato to cook it.

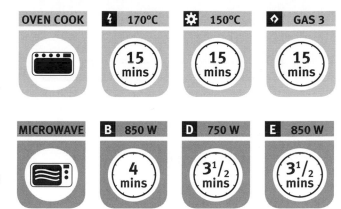

Symbols for cooking food.

Cooking symbols

These are symbols for heating food that you find on packaging. They show the time and temperature required to cook products and indicate whether you should use a cooker or a microwave.

Cookers and ovens

Fan-assisted ovens

In fan-assisted ovens, the convection currents are disturbed as the fan moves the hot air around, instead of it rising to the top of the oven. The temperature is the same in all parts of the oven, so food cooks for the same amount of time on each of the shelves. This is useful when you are cooking a batch of biscuits and cakes, as they should all be ready in a similar time. In other ovens, the food on the shelves cooks at different temperatures, so the food on the top cooks the fastest.

Features for a cooker

- A thermostat turns the oven on and off and selects the temperature chosen for cooking.
- A timer sets the oven to be turned on and off automatically at pre-set times.
- A temperature probe can switch off the oven when the food is completely cooked.

TO DO

Compare the speed of cooking a tray of biscuits in a fan-assisted oven and in an ordinary oven. Get the oven ready to use by setting the temperature. Put the biscuits on two or three trays and place them in the two ovens at the same time. After about 10 minutes, take out the biscuits and compare results.

QUESTIONS

1. Give three reasons for cooking food.
2. Which of the three methods of heat transfer are used to:
   a) boil a potato in a metal pan in boiling water on top of the stove
   b) bake a cake in an oven
   c) cook some toast under the grill?
3. Explain why it is best to:
   a) stir food with a wooden spoon rather than a metal spoon
   b) use an oven glove to lift a baking tray out of the hot oven.

Cooking methods 2

Different ways of cooking food are used to increase the palatability and flavour of food.

Cooking with water

Water-soluble vitamins B and C can be lost from vegetables during cooking in water.

Cooking method	Advantages
Boiling in water for vegetables	Quick method that can save water-soluble vitamins
Stewing: cooking meat, vegetables and fruit in liquid	Slower method but can lose water-soluble vitamins
Steaming in steamers over boiling water	Vegetables do not lose vitamins in cooking water
Pressure cooking: cooks food in liquid above boiling point	Quick method of cooking, helps to save the loss of water-soluble vitamins

Cooking with fat

Frying in fat cooks food at a higher temperature than water. The food cooks quickly so vitamins are not lost, but frying increases the fat content and energy value.

- **Shallow frying** is cooking food in a little fat, such as fried eggs.
- **Deep-fat frying** is used for foods like fish and chips, which are cooked in plenty of hot fat.
- **Roasting food** in an oven is used to cook meat and vegetables. Fat is poured over the food as it cooks.

Microwave cooking

A **microwave** is used for reheating ready-made food, cooking vegetables and fish, and defrosting frozen food. The microwaves inside the oven penetrate the food to 3–5 cm. Energy is absorbed by the food, especially the fat and water molecules. The molecules become agitated and vibrate, and this heat cooks the food. Microwaves do not cook food evenly. Cold areas are called cold spots. A rotating turntable turns the food so that microwaves can penetrate around the food. To cook evenly, food needs stirring.

WEBSITES

Microwave Technologies Association

Frying adds fat to food.

FACT

The first domestic microwave was sold in the UK in 1974.

KEY TERMS

Microwaves waves that vibrate the fat and water molecules producing heat

Advantages and disadvantage of different cooking methods

Method of cooking	Advantages	Disadvantages
Boiling or stewing	Quick and no fat	Water-soluble vitamins are lost. Can damage the structure of food
Steaming	Quick and no fat	May steam up kitchen
Pressure cooking	Very quick and uses less fuel	Food is not very tasty
Stir-frying	Food keeps crunchy texture. Less loss of water soluble vitamins	Some fat is added
Microwave	Quick, using little fuel. Less loss of vitamins	May not get good flavours and can be overcooked
Frying	Food is crisp and tasty	Adds fat to food
Grilling	Quick and reduces fat content	Can burn if not watched
Baking	Adds flavour and essential method for baking cakes and bread. Does not increase fat content	Takes a long time
Roasting	Adds flavour and texture	Takes a long time. Adds fat. Vitamins C and D are lost

Rules for microwaves

- Always reheat food until it is piping hot and reaches 72°C for two minutes.
- Overheat rather than underheat, so food reaches a high temperature.
- Metal containers cannot be used, as they reflect microwaves and cause sparking.
- Use special microwave clingfilms.

Microwave cookers use little energy.

Advantages of microwave ovens

- They can be used for thawing, cooking and reheating.
- Cooking is very fast and uses little energy.
- You can prepare snacks and meals easily and save on washing up.
- Food keeps its quality, taste and nutrients during reheating.
- There is little waste, and food can be cooked from frozen.
- Vitamin C of vegetables is higher than boiled vegetables, as cooking time is shorter and less water is added.

QUESTIONS

1. Explain the difference between:
   a) boiling and steaming vegetables
   b) roasting and baking potatoes.
2. How does a microwave oven cook food?
3. Give three advantages of using a microwave for cooking.

Effect of heat on food

Heating food can affect the nutrients within it, and alter its
food's nutritional values.

Effect of heating on macronutrients

Macro nutrients	Effect of heating	How is this used in cooking process?	Nutritional changes	Found in
Starch	Starch turns to dextrin in dry heat. In liquid, starch granules swell and absorb liquid – called gelatinisation.	Forms the crust in bread and cakes. Thickens soups and sauces. Dextrin in bread makes the loaf crust crispy and turns toast golden brown.	Carbohydrate value is not lost unless the food is burnt.	Cereals such as wheat, and root vegetables such as potatoes.
Sugar	Sugar dissolves, changes colour and caramelises to a brown colour.	Used to colour syrups and make caramel. Sugar on a crème brulee is browned under the grill or with a blowtorch.	Carbohydrate value is not lost unless the food is burnt.	Sucrose, which is made from sugar beet or sugar cane.
Fats	Solid fats melt to liquid and give off smoke and burn at high temperatures. Fats have different melting temperatures.	Fats can be used for frying but those with higher melting temperatures fry food better.	Fat is not changed in value unless it is burnt.	Butter, lard, margarine; oils – corn, sunflower, soya bean and olive oil.
Protein	Protein denatures and changes on heating, then coagulates and sets.	Proteins in eggs coagulate and set when heated and become solid. Meat hardens.	Protein value is not lost unless the protein is burnt.	Eggs, cheese, milk, flour, meat, fish, beans and pulses.
Dietary fibre	Fibre softens when it is heated with liquid.	Cabbage softens when it is cooked.	Dietary fibre remains undigestible after cooking.	Cereals, fruit and vegetables.

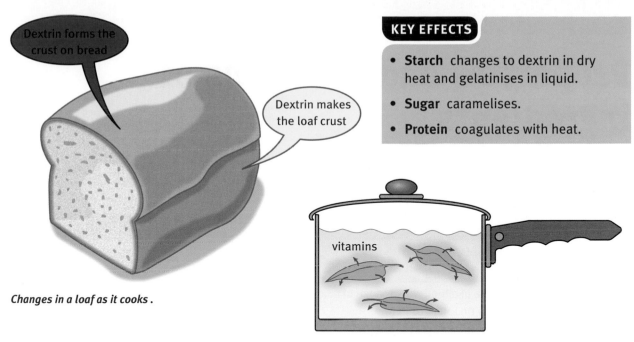

Dextrin forms the crust on bread

Dextrin makes the loaf crust

Changes in a loaf as it cooks .

KEY EFFECTS

- **Starch** changes to dextrin in dry heat and gelatinises in liquid.
- **Sugar** caramelises.
- **Protein** coagulates with heat.

vitamins

Water-soluble vitamins B and C are lost in cooking.

Effect of heating on micronutrients: minerals and vitamins

Micronutrients	Effect of heating	How is this used in cooking process?	Nutritional changes
Vitamins – fat-soluble A and D	Fat-soluble vitamins are not affected by the cooking process.		Fat-soluble vitamins are not lost in cooking.
Vitamins – water-soluble B and C	Water-soluble vitamins B and C dissolve in water. High temperature cooking such as frying destroys these vitamins.	Vitamin C is easily lost when preparing and cooking vegetables. Avoid long cooking and keeping vegetables warm.	Water-soluble vitamins are lost during cooking. Vitamin C is lost if fruit and vegetables are stored for too long.
Minerals	Heating has little effect on minerals.		There is little mineral loss during cooking.

QUESTIONS

1. Describe the changes that take place when the following nutrients are heated:
   a) starch
   b) sugar
   c) fat
   d) protein
   e) dietary fibre.
2. What happens when vitamins and minerals are heated?

Properties and functions of ingredients

Food ingredients have properties that are used in many ways when preparing food.

Properties and functions of different food ingredients	
Properties and functions	**Examples**
Adding colour	People like food with a range of colours. You can add garnish to colour a dish, such as a cherry on top of custard.
Adding flavour	Salt, pepper, herbs and spices improve flavour in savoury dishes. Strong-flavoured foods such as cheese, bacon and tomatoes add flavour to sauces and pasta dishes. Chocolate adds flavour to sweet dishes.
Adding texture	You might want to add crunch in a salad or to a smooth pasta dish. Peas add colour and texture to a rice dish; fresh chunks of fruit improve the texture of a milky dessert.
Aerating	This means making food lighter by adding a gas such as air, carbon dioxide or steam. You can whisk eggs to add air, or use raising agents such as yeast to introduce carbon dioxide gas.
Binding	Dry ingredients need binding so that they stick together. You can add water or eggs to bind things together, as with beefburgers or veggie burgers and pastry.
Bulking	Some foods make up the main carbohydrate part of the recipe and add volume. These are inexpensive ingredients such as flour and sugar, which are used in pastries and sweets.
Emulsifying	Ingredients such as eggs help other liquids to hold together, as in making mayonnaise from oil and vinegar.
Glazing	Egg is used to give a shiny, glazed finish to pastry, and honey glazes cooked meats.
Preserving	Ingredients can help other foods to keep longer. Sugar is needed to preserve fruit, and vinegar preserves vegetables. Fish can be salted to increase the keeping time.
Setting food	Gelatine is used to set jellies. Cold sauces such as blancmange are set with cornflour, and other sauces may use starch products such as flour. Egg is used to set a flan.
Shortening	Fats and oils help to shorten a flour mixture such as pastry, and make it crisp and crumbly in texture.
Sweetening	Sugar is the main ingredient used to sweeten dishes. Dried fruits such as raisins, apricots and figs add sweetness. Honey and jam can also be used.
Thickening	Flours, starchy vegetables and bread are used to thicken sauces, soups and stews.

TO DO

Fit the function to the ingredient

For the chicken pie and muesli, fit the function to the ingredient.

pastry

filling, including sauce and chicken

Chicken pie
- Pastry made with flour, fat and water
- Chicken filling – white sauce made with milk, butter and flour
- Chicken with mushrooms, salt and pepper

Functions: binding ingredients together, thickening ingredients, adding flavour

Muesli
Oats, nuts, dried fruit, dried banana

Functions: bulking, sweetener, adding texture, adding colour

Properties and the foods that provide them

Properties	Fats	Eggs	Pulses	Cereals	Fruit	Sugar	Milk	Flour	Oil
Aerating	✓	✓				✓			
Binding	✓	✓		✓			✓	✓	✓
Drowning	✓	✓		✓		✓	✓	✓	✓
Emulsifying		✓							
Flavouring	✓	✓	✓		✓	✓	✓		✓
Moistening	✓	✓			✓	✓	✓		✓
Preserving	✓					✓			✓
Setting		✓						✓	
Shortening	✓								✓
Stabilising		✓						✓	
Sweetening					✓	✓			
Thickening		✓	✓	✓	✓		✓	✓	

QUESTIONS

1. Give two examples of ingredients that perform each of these functions:
   a) aerating
   b) binding dry ingredients
   c) setting desserts
   d) thickening a sauce.
2. Describe four dishes that use each of these four functions.

Properties and functions: Flour

Flour is made from starchy cereals and plants:

- wheat flour – wheat
- cornflour – maize
- potato flour – potatoes
- rice flour – rice.

Starch gelatinisation

Raw starch tastes floury so it needs to be cooked. When starch and liquid are heated, the liquid passes through the cell walls of the starch granules, which burst. This process is called **gelatinisation**. At about 60°C, starch granules begin to absorb liquid and, as the mixture gets hotter, the granules swell and make a paste with the liquid – the paste is called a gel.

If the mixture is undercooked, it has a grainy texture and tastes starchy.

When starch has gelatinised, baked products have a good texture and volume, and sauces and soup thicken. If thickened liquid is left to cool or is frozen, the gel leaks – a process called retrogradation, when water is forced out of the gel structure.

Starch gelatinises when heated.

TO DO

Basic sauce recipe: 30 g wheat flour, 300 ml water

Prepare a sauce with some water and wheat flour. Stir the mixture in a saucepan over the heat and let it thicken. Make sauces from other flours such as cornflour, rice flour and potato flour. Compare the results for thickness and clearness, and write a report on your findings to show the thickening ability of different starches.

Gluten in flour

Gluten is formed when proteins in wheat flour called gliadin and glutenin join together when water is added. Many cereals contain gluten, the protein that forms the structure of bread and cakes. The amount of gluten varies with the type

WEBSITES

Flour Advisory Bureau

of flour. When flour dough mixtures are heated, the dough is pushed up and the gluten sets, forming the framework of the baked product.

Bread must be made with special, high-gluten flour. Strong bread-making flours contain the most gluten. Gluten is stretchy and elastic and, as it is worked during kneading of bread and pastry making, it becomes stronger and smoother. During baking, proteins coagulate to make the solid, risen product.

People with coeliac disease must avoid foods containing gluten.

KEY TERMS

Gelatinisation when starch breaks down when heated with water to thicken mixtures

Gluten the protein formed when wheat flour is mixed with liquid

Browning when starch is heated to a high temperature

INVESTIGATION

Compare the gluten in different flours. You need strong, plain and self-raising flour.

Mix 100 g of each flour with enough water to form a dough ball. Wrap each ball in a J cloth and run water over the dough. The starch runs out into the water. Squeeze until no more starch comes out. You can pull the gluten ball to see how it stretches and shrinks.

Bake the gluten balls in a hot oven until they are puffed up and golden. Compare sizes. Strong flour should make the largest ball as it contains the most gluten.

Browning

Starch helps to make baked products such as bread and cakes golden brown, known as **browning**. When you make toast, the bread turns brown as starch reacts with the protein in the wheat under high heat. If you heat starch too much it will become black and burnt.

QUESTIONS

1. Name three types of flour and where they are used in cooking.
2. What is meant by the terms:
   a) gelatinisation
   b) gluten
   c) retrogradation
   d) browning?
3. What type of flour is commonly used for bread-making and why?

Properties and functions: Sugar

When **sugar** (sucrose) is extracted from sugar beet or cane juice, a black syrup, known as molasses, remains. When white sugar is made, the molasses are removed. Brown sugars keep some of this natural syrup.

Types of sugar

White sugar is used in many ways.

- Granulated sugar is used to sweeten drinks and sprinkle on foods.
- Caster sugar is finer and used for cake and biscuit making.
- Icing sugar is a fine powder and used for sweets and icing.
- Brown sugars have a strong flavour and are used for biscuits and cakes.

Functions of sugar in cooking

- Sweetens foods such as stewed apple.
- Improves the flavour of some foods, such as tomato ketchup.
- Helps colour foods as sugar caramelises when heated and turns brown, so is used in baked products, when the sugar browns foods such as cakes and biscuits.
- Helps to aerate food and make foams. Used in cakes to make them light and risen. When whisked with egg white to make meringues, sugar makes the foam stable.
- Helps food to stay moist and tender, and increases shelf life of bread and cakes as the sugar helps food products stay moist.
- Sugar reduces gluten development in flour, so cakes and biscuits are tender.
- Helps fermentation by adding to yeast to speed up the production of carbon dioxide gas in bread doughs.
- Preserves in jams and chutney to keep the products for a long time.
- Used for sweets by boiling to different temperatures to make a range of sweets such as toffee, fudge and boiled sweets.
- Adds volume to food products as a **bulking agent**.

Changing the sugar in a recipe

Use dried fruit and artificial sweeteners as well as sugar substitutes to replace sugar in recipes – but this needs care.

Different types of sugar.

If you lower the amount of sugar in jams, you reduce the length of time that they will keep, as sugar is the preservative.

If you adapt a cake recipe, sugar may make the product light and form part of the structure, so you must test the recipe, which may go wrong.

Dried fruits and artificial sweetener.

TO DO

These are the ingredients for carrot cake. Which ingredients make the cake and icing sweet?

Ingredients

Cake: brown sugar, carrot, wheat flour, vegetable oil, mixed fruit & peel (sultanas, currants, raisins, orange peel, lemon peel), egg, desiccated coconut, bicarbonate of soda, cinnamon, salt.
Icing: icing sugar, cream cheese, double cream, salt, stabiliser (sodium alginate), unsalted butter.

How to store and cook

Carrot cake.

INVESTIGATION

Investigate how you can lower the sugar in a basic cake or biscuit recipe. Experiment with low sugar products and intense sweeteners as well as dried fruits and honey. Read the instructions, as many of the intense sweeteners cannot be used in baking. Analyse your recipe to find the sugar in 100 grams in the basic recipe and in the new recipe.

These two products can be used in recipes to lower the sugar content.

- Splenda Brown Sugar Blend – made from sugar, molasses, sweetener (sucralose), humectant (glycerol), flavourings, stabiliser (xanthan gum).
- Fruisana Fruit Sugar – made from pure fructose. Fructose is sweeter than ordinary sugar so you need to use a third less. Fruisana is an ingredient that can replace ordinary sugar.

Fruisana fruit sugar.

QUESTIONS

What is the function of sugar in the following products?
a) strawberry jam
b) tomato ketchup
c) fruit cake
d) meringues
e) scones.

Properties and functions: Fats

We use fats to spread on bread and in cooking, to fry and roast food. People should cut down on the amount of fat that they eat, especially fats high in **saturated fat**, which are linked to heart disease.

Types of fat

- **Margarine:** Made from a range of animal and vegetable fats. Can be hardened by hydrogenation, which makes the fats saturated. Used for spreading, cakes and baking.

- **Reduced-fat spreads:** Contain 40–80 per cent fat compared with margarine and butter, which are 80 per cent fat. Designed to be used in lower-fat diets. Used for spreading, but have too much water in them to be used for frying, roasting and baking.

- **Lard:** Made from pig's fat and used for pastry and frying. High in saturated fat, which can be bad for your health. Not suitable for Muslims, Jews or vegetarians.

- **Suet:** Made from fat from animals. Used for dumplings and puddings. Vegetarian 'suet', made from non-animal fat, is now more popular.

- **Butter:** Made by churning cream. High in saturated fat, which should be reduced. Used for spreading, baking, frying and roasting. Ghee is clarified, unsalted butter used in Asian cooking.

- **Oil:** Oil is fat which is liquid at room temperature. Seeds and nuts are used to make oil and include corn, soya and rapeseed oils. Oil is used in dressings, frying baking and roasting.

- **Solid vegetable fats:** Used for pastry, since they produce a crisp pastry. These fats are used instead of lard as they contain less saturated fat.

Range of fats.

Properties of fat in cooking
Shortening

Fats shorten baked products, such as pastry and shortbread by making them soft and crumbly. For shortcrust pastry, fat is mixed with flour. The fat forms a protective coating around the flour protein, which helps to make a shorter mixture when cooked.

> **KEY TERMS**
>
> **Saturated fat** fat that is linked to heart disease
>
> **Shortening** fats used to make baked products crumbly

> **FACT**
>
> In 1869, a prize was offered to invent a product like butter, so margarine was invented.

Aeration

When fat such as margarine and butter are creamed with sugar, the mixture holds air, making a stable foam.

Frying

Lard used to be popular for frying, but generally people do not want to eat animal fats, so vegetable oils are used instead. Fats with a high smoke point, such as vegetable oil, are good for frying, as the high temperature seals the food and makes it crisp.

Smoke points of fat	
Fat	Smoke point
Lard	205°C
Most vegetable oils – not olive oil	232°C
Vegetable shortenings	188° C

Percentages of fat and saturated fat, and which fats are suitable for vegetarians			
Food	% fat	% saturated fat	Vegetarian?
Butter	82	57	✓
Margarine (hard)	75	28	✓
Soya spread	59	14	✓
Lard	99	44	
Vegetable suet	62	29	✓
Beef suet	87	46	
Reduced-fat spread	59	14	✓
Vegetable oil	100	14.5	✓

INVESTIGATION

Use food labels or the Internet to find out what type of fat you would use for the following methods of cooking. Give two examples for each method.

- Pastry making
- Cake making
- Frying
- Roasting
- Spreading

Test and compare fats for pastry making. Test out pastry made with butter, margarine or a mix of several fats. Taste-test the results and find the best.

QUESTIONS

1. Name two fats that are made from animal products.
2. Name two fats that are suitable for vegetarians.
3. Name a fat that can be used for:
   a) cake making
   b) pastry making
   c) frying food.
4. Use the table that shows the percentage of fat. Which fat contains the most fat, and which contains the least saturated fat?

Raising agents

Raising agents are added to sweet and savoury mixtures to make them rise and give lightness to a dough.

How do raising agents work?

The raising agent produces bubbles of gas. In a hot oven or steamer, the gas expands, pushing up the mixture. Some gas escapes and some is trapped in the mixture as it cooks and sets.

Different raising agents

There are three types of raising agent: air, steam and carbon dioxide.

Air

How is air introduced into mixtures?

- Sieving flour to make scones and cakes.
- Beating eggs for batters and cakes.
- Whisking egg whites to make meringues.
- Creaming fat and sugar to make cakes.
- Rubbing fat into flour for pastries and scones.
- Rolling and folding pastry.

Raising agents are needed for bread, cakes and biscuits.

Steam

Water changes to steam when it reaches boiling point at 100°C. Batters, used for Yorkshire pudding, contain a lot of water and, as it cooks, the steam escapes and pushes up the mixture. Steam is a raising agent in breads, some cakes and choux pastry.

Carbon dioxide

This is produced in two ways.

- **Chemical raising agents** – baking powder and bicarbonate of soda release carbon dioxide gas. Self-raising flour is ready mixed with baking powder and saves you measuring the raising agent.
- **Yeast** – a single-celled fungus that needs food, warmth and liquid to ferment to produce carbon dioxide gas.

Yeast is a raising agent used in bread.

> **KEY TERMS**
>
> **Raising agents** added to make mixtures rise

Bread-making

Most breads are made with yeast. The dough increases in size as the yeast ferments to produce carbon dioxide. This process is called proving when the dough is left in a warm place so that the yeast grows. During baking, the carbon dioxide pushes up the dough and makes the bread rise.

INVESTIGATION

1. Find out how baking powder and bicarbonate of soda work.

   Put 2 teaspoons of baking powder and bicarbonate of soda in 2 cups and pour some warm water into each cup to about 3 cm deep. Watch what happens. See the mixture bubbling as it gives off carbon dioxide gas. Taste each mixture. You will find that the bicarbonate of soda tastes soapy when it stops bubbling. It is only used in strong tasting recipes such as gingerbread to disguise its flavour.

2. Find out how yeast ferments to produce carbon dioxide gas. You need a packet of dried yeast and some sugar. Put a teaspoon of the dried yeast into a cup and add some sugar (food) and warm water (to help it grow). Stir the mixture and leave it in a warm place. The yeast begins to bubble and give off carbon dioxide gas and it smells like beer.

WEBSITES

HowStuffWorks

TO DO

Find five recipes that each use baking powder, bicarbonate of soda and yeast. That's 15 recipes altogether. How is the raising agent added to each recipe? Keep a record of your findings.

QUESTIONS

1. What are the three types of raising agent?
2. How does baking powder and bicarbonate of soda work?
3. How does yeast work?
4. Name a product that uses:
   a) baking powder
   b) bicarbonate of soda
   c) yeast.

Changes that take place in cooking

Shortcrust pastry

Shortcrust pastry is made from plain flour, fat (choice of lard, margarine or white fat), salt and water. To make the pastry, rub the fat into the flour and add cold water to mix to a dough.

Steak pie: 690 kcal.

Ingredient	Function
Plain flour – wheat	Absorbs the fat, forms the structure, is able to stretch, not too high in gluten, gives a crisp, light texture when cooked.
Fat – lard	Has a shortening effect by forming a thin film round flour particles, which reduces the amount of water that can mix with flour. Gives a light, crumbly texture and forms a thin film round the flour particles – but made from animal fat.
Margarine	Has a shortening effect, which reduces the amount of water that can mix with flour. Adds flavour and colour.
Water	Binds the dry ingredients together, works with the gluten to stretch the dough, gives lightness and acts as a raising agent.
Salt	Works with the gluten and provides flavour.

White sauce

White sauce is made from plain flour, butter or margarine, milk and seasoning (salt and pepper). To make the white sauce by the 'all in one' method, put all the ingredients in a saucepan, then heat and stir until thick.

Ingredient	Function
Plain flour – wheat	Flour granules absorb liquid when heated to form a paste called a gel. Granules swell and thicken liquid – called gelatinisation. Overcooking can cause gel to squeeze out liquid – retrogradation.
Butter or margarine	Adds flavour and colour and a glossy finish. Prevents lumps forming in sauces. Fat surrounds the flour particles and allow them to mix with liquid for smooth result.
Milk	Milk proteins can coagulate on heating.
Salt and pepper	Provides flavour and taste.

Ingredients and techniques that cause problems

If you add acid ingredients to the sauce, such as lemon juice and tomatoes or grated cheese, the sauce may curdle and the mixture separate.

Chilling or freezing a sauce made from flour will make the gel break up and liquid seep out. This is called retrogradation.

Biscuits

Simple biscuits or creamed cakes such as fairy cakes are made from self-raising flour, fat (butter or margarine), sugar and egg.

To make the biscuits, fat is creamed with sugar and then mixed with egg and flour.

Ingredient	Function
Self raising flour – wheat	Absorbs the fat, forms the structure, gives a crisp, light texture when cooked. Carbon dioxide gas is given off as a raising agent which lightens the biscuit.
Fat – butter	Has a shortening effect by forming a thin film round flour particles, which reduces the amount of water that can mix with flour. Gives a crumbly, melt in the mouth texture. Adds flavour and colour.
Margarine	Has a shortening effect that reduces the amount of water that can mix with flour. Adds flavour and colour. Less expensive than butter.
Sugar	Adds sweetness and improves flavour. Helps to colour products. Helps to make the mixture lighter as it helps trap air. Helps the biscuit stay moist.
Eggs	Binds the dry ingredients together. Sets (coagulates) to form the structure.
Salt	Works with the gluten and provides flavour.

QUESTION

For each of the recipes on pages 124–125, give two functions for each of the ingredients.

Acids and alkalis in cooking

Acids and alkalis are measured using a scale called the **pH scale**. The lower the number, the more acidic the food – so lemon juice with a pH of 2.4 is acidic.

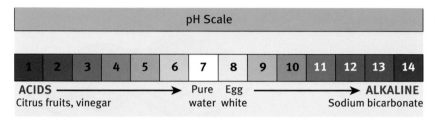

pH Scale													
1	2	3	4	5	6	7	8	9	10	11	12	13	14

ACIDS ⟶ Pure   Egg ⟶ ALKALINE
Citrus fruits, vinegar   water white   Sodium bicarbonate

pH scale to show acidity and alkalinity of food

KEY TERMS

pH scale the scale for measuring acids and alkalis

Here are the pH values of some foods:

- lemon juice: 2.4 pH (most acidic)
- vinegar: 2.8 pH
- cream of tartar: 3.0 to 4.0 pH
- milk: 6.8 pH
- water: 7.0 pH (neutral)
- baking soda: 9.0 pH (least acidic).

Acids

Acid foods include lemon juice, tomatoes, vinegar and cream of tartar.

Alkalis

In cooking, the most common alkali used is bicarbonate of soda, known as baking soda. Adding baking soda to the water when cooking green vegetables helps maintain their bright colour because it neutralises the natural acid in the vegetables. However, it also destroys some of the vegetable's vitamin C so should *never* be used.

Baking soda is used to help make baked goods rise. It neutralises acid ingredients (such as molasses, buttermilk and honey) and produces well-risen cakes and scones.

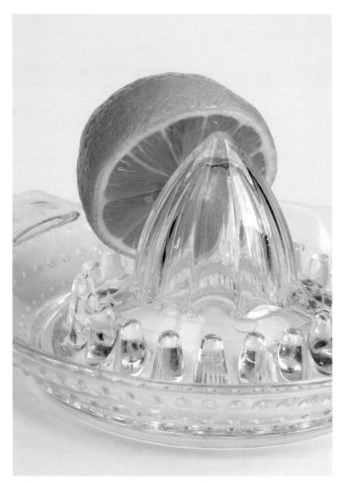

Lemons are acid; they have a pH of 2.4.

Effects of acids and alkalis on foods

What the acid food does	How it works
Stops fruit turning brown. When fruit such as bananas, apples and pears are cut, they begin to turn brown. This is caused by enzymes in the fruit linking with oxygen in air. It is called enzymic browning and causes loss of vitamin C.	If acid foods such as citric acid from lemon juice are added to the fruit this prevents browning.
Makes a sauce separate.	Acid foods can make a sauce which has been made from thickened starch, separate and curdle. So if lemon juice or tomatoes are added to the white sauce, the sauce will change consistency.
Tenderises meat.	Acid food such as lemon juice and yogurt can tenderise meat by being used as a marinade and spread over the raw meat before it is cooked.
Helps whisked egg whites to foam.	When whisking egg whites, adding a small amount of acid, such as cream of tartar, lemon juice or vinegar, stabilises the egg whites and allows them to reach their full volume and stiffness by making the egg coagulate faster.
When lemon or lime juice is added to raw fish it 'cooks' it.	Ceviche (a South American dish of raw seafood) is marinated in a citrus-based mixture, with lemons and limes. The citric acid causes the proteins in the seafood to denature, which 'cooks' the fish without heat.
Helps to preserve food.	Adding vinegar to vegetables such as pickles prevents bacteria from multiplying as the mixture is too acid.
Reduces the thickening power of starch.	Acid foods such a tomatoes and lemon juice break down starch granules and reduce the thickening power of starch in a sauce.

QUESTIONS

1. Give two examples to show how acids are used during food preparation.
2. In each example, explain how the acid changes the food.
3. Why should bicarbonate of soda *not* be used to brighten the colour of green vegetables?

Cooking equipment

Many types of **labour-saving machinery** help us to save time in the kitchen.

These include:

- food processors
- bread machines
- blenders and electric whisks.

Do these things really help and are they good value for money?

In the UK, organisations such as Which? and Good Housekeeping compare equipment and services so people can make the best buy. For research, they test a number of gadgets, looking at different features, and write a report to show the best buy in terms of price, design and how well it works.

The example that follows shows an investigation for bread-making machines.

Bread-making machine

What questions should you ask?

- How does the price compare?
- What accessories are included and what is their quality?
- Kneading paddle – is it easy to remove?

Bread-making machine.

KEY TERMS

Labour-saving machinery machinery designed to save time and effort

Gadgets pieces of equipment that may or may not be useful in food preparation

TO DO

Work in groups to carry out a practical assessment of a piece of small kitchen machinery. Your group can choose a food processor, hand blender, juicer, sandwich toaster or waffle iron – or any other piece of labour-saving equipment. Find out the price and make a list of questions that you want to investigate. Look at the features and the range of tasks that the equipment can perform. Test the machinery to see how well it carries out practical tasks. Present your findings as a consumer report.

'Sales of breadmakers boom as price of loaf rises by 20%'

'Britons spend billions on useless gadgets'

- Viewing window – can you see what is going on?
- Programming – is there an easy to use control panel?
- Baking choices – can you bake gluten-free bread, cake and jam, and make pasta?
- How long is the baking cycle?
- Is it easy to clean?

Carry out tests to find out how well it bakes a loaf of bread and compare with other machines.

WEBSITES

Which?

INVESTIGATION

Carry out some research to find the most popular kitchen **gadgets**. Find the reasons why some gadgets are more useful than others. Choose from this list and add your own – food processors, bread-making machines, blenders, electric whisks, toasters, electric knife, juicers, ice cream makers, deep-fat fryers, rice cookers, waffle irons.

QUESTIONS

Give your views

Copy and complete this list of kitchen equipment. For each item, explain how it saves time, then say if it really is useful. One example has been completed and you can add your own ideas.

Gadget	How does it save time?	Is it really useful?
Food blender	Helps to make soup smooth and saves time because you would have to sieve the food to make it smooth.	Yes.
Hand whisk		
Toaster		
Bread-making machine		
Microwave		
Electric knife		
Pasta machine		
Juicer		
Rice cooker		
Waffle maker		

ExamCafé

Welcome

This chapter includes many types of food.

Draw up a quick revision table such as the one below and fill in the cells.

You will need to learn the nutritional value of each food type, and other special points – list three in this section for your revision notes. For example, eggs have lots of uses in cooking such as thickening.

	Nutrition value	Special points
Meat and poultry		
Fish		
Eggs		Plenty of uses in cooking
Milk, cheese		
New protein – TVP, Quorn™		
Fruit and vegetables		
Beans and pulses		
Potatoes		
Cereals		

For each part of the chapter, copy and complete a different table. For each of the three topics below, list three functions for that food. See 'Scones' on the following page for an example.

	Food	Functions
Properties and functions of flour		
Properties and functions of sugar		
Properties and functions of fats		

When this table is complete, it will help you to describe the changes that take place when cooking different food products and dishes. You can draw them like a spider diagram.

Scones

Flour – function – bulk – provides structure
Margarine or butter – function – adds moisture – adds flavour
Milk or liquid – function – binds together
Try this for other popular foods. But choose ones that are well known, as these are the ones likely to be chosen in the exam – for example, pastry, cakes, biscuits, bread and white sauce. Here are some examples of the questions that could be asked on this section, and suggested answers. Remember: look at the marks and write enough points to get those marks.

Question 1

Give three reasons for cooking food (3 marks).

Answer 1

Cooking food – choose any three.
- To make food safe to eat by destroying bacteria.
- To improve the texture and flavour.
- To make the food hot.
- To make a dish which is attractive to eat.
- To make raw food such as meat and fish edible.
- To kill off moulds, yeasts and enzymes and make the food keep longer.

Question 2

Explain the meaning of the following terms:
Conduction (2 marks); Convection (2 marks); Radiation (2 marks).

Answer 2

Conduction – need 2 points
Conduction is where heat is conducted from molecule to molecule in solids or liquids.
- Boiling conducts heat through liquids.
- Heat is conducted through metal pans and cooking trays.
- Metal is a good conductor of heat.

Convection – need 2 points
Convection is where heat travels round liquids and air by convection currents.
Convection currents flow around an oven as hot air rises and cold air falls.
Convection currents flow in a pan of water as heat is passed through the water.

Radiation – need 2 points
Radiation is where heat travels in waves or rays. Grilling is an example of radiation. Heat travels by infra-red rays, which are absorbed and heat up the food.

Question 3

Name the method of heat transfer and explain how you would get a quality result when
a) grilling bacon (3 marks),
b) baking a potato (3 marks).

Answer 3

Grilling bacon
Grilling is cooking by radiation; heat travels in waves to the food, then heat is conducted through the bacon.
To get a quality result:
- preheat the grill
- make sure the bacon cooks evenly
- turn the bacon if needed
- do not burn.

Baking a potato
This is cooked by convection currents in the oven, then heat is conducted through the potato.
To get a quality result:
- choose a baking potato to give best results
- prepare the potato beforehand by washing and making a cut
- preheat the oven – you could microwave the potato first to save time and money
- check with a sharp knife to see if it is soft and take out when done.

Food spoilage 1

Food spoilage is caused by micro-organisms, which are too small to see without the use of a microscope. The three types of micro-organism are **yeasts**, **bacteria** and **moulds**.

Yeasts

Yeasts are microscopic, single-celled fungi that reproduce by budding. Yeasts use sugar to grow and produce carbon dioxide gas, in the process called fermentation.

Yeasts can attack foods such as jams and cause spoilage, but they are useful in making many food products such as bread and beer. Through fermentation, they help bread to rise and change grapes into wine. Yeasts are killed by heat.

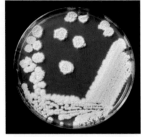
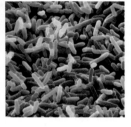

Bacteria, yeast and mould cause food spoilage.

Bacteria

Bacteria are single-celled organisms that are widely found in soil, in air and on our bodies. Some bacteria are useful to us, and others cause food spoilage and serious illness. Useful bacteria are used to make foods such as yogurt and cheese. Most bacteria are killed by heat.

Moulds

Moulds are a form of fungus. Mould spores are carried in the air. They settle and grow on the surfaces of food such as bread, meat and cheese. Mould is used in the production of some foods such as blue cheese.

Certain moulds produce harmful toxins – for example, the mould that grows on peanuts produces aflotoxin, which causes serious illness and even death, if eaten. Moulds are killed by heat.

Enzymes

Enzymes are not micro-organisms, but chemicals that can be found in food. Enzymes can change food: they cause fruits such as apples to go brown, and can destroy the vitamin content of food. Enzymes are destroyed by heat.

KEY TERMS

Yeasts fungi that ferment

Bacteria single-celled organisms that are useful, but can be harmful

Moulds a form of fungi

Enzymes chemicals in food that cause changes

High-risk foods foods that can only be stored for a short time before they become unsafe to eat

WEBSITES

Food Standards Agency

The effects of micro-organisms on foods

Micro-organism	Useful functions	Harmful functions
Yeasts	Yeasts ferment to make beer, wine and bread.	Fermented food can taste sour and have off flavours.
Bacteria	Bacteria are used to make cheese and yogurt.	Pathogenic bacteria cause food poisoning.
Moulds	Blue cheese has mould added to it.	Moulds turn food such as bread mouldy.
Enzymes – chemicals	Used to change the structure of some food products.	Cause browning of apples and loss of vitamins.

Food-poisoning bacteria can enter food at any stage during production, shopping, storage and cooking of food.

To enable them to grow, bacteria need:

- time to grow
- the correct temperature
- food and moisture.

If one or more of these conditions is removed, there is less chance for bacteria to grow.

Food and moisture control

Bacteria like moist, high-protein foods such as meat, chicken, fish and dairy products. These are called '**high-risk foods**' as they can only be stored for a short time before they go off and become unsafe to eat.

High-risk foods.

Foods can be preserved so that the moisture/water is unavailable for bacteria to multiply.

Food	Where is the water?
Frozen food	The water is frozen, so it is not available.
Dried food	The water has been dried off.

QUESTIONS

1. Name the three types of micro-organism that cause food spoilage. For each type, give an example of how it causes food spoilage.
2. Give four examples of how micro-organisms are useful in food production.
3. Explain why frozen and dried food does not go off.

Food spoilage 2

Time control

Time control is important during preparation, storage, cooking and reheating.

Some bacteria divide in two every ten minutes by a process called binary fission. After two or three hours, food that contained a few food poisoning bacteria will contain enough to cause illness.

> **Time: dos and don'ts**
>
> - The length of time that food is kept in the danger zone (5-63°C) should be as short as possible so that bacteria do not begin to multiply quickly.
> - The time between buying the food to storing in the refrigerator or freezer should be as short as possible.
> - Food must not be kept past its 'use-by' or 'best before' date, when it might be unsafe to eat.

Temperature control

This is the most effective way to control or destroy bacteria.

The danger zone – 5–63°C

Bacteria grow rapidly at 20–50°C, so to prevent their growth, food should be kept below 5°C and cooked to above 63°C. However, some bacteria can produce spores that survive above 63°C. For food safety, keep perishable, high-risk food out of the **danger zone**.

Keep food cool

If food is kept cool in a refrigerator, the bacteria are not killed, but their growth is slowed down. Refrigerators should operate at 5°C or below. This can be checked using a refrigerator thermometer.

Keeping food in freezers can stop bacteria growing but does not kill them, so once the food is defrosted, the bacteria can multiply in warm conditions.

The 2006 Food Hygiene Regulations require that most short-life food is stored at 8°C or colder when it is being processed,

KEY TERMS

Danger zone the temperature range 5–63°C, when food can be spoiled and become dangerous to eat

Food probe a cookery instrument used to measure the temperature inside food

Keep the refrigerator at 5°C and less, and the freezer at -18°C.

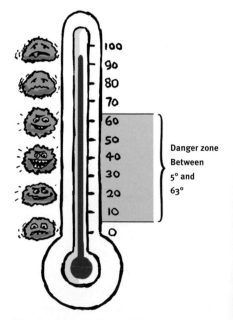

The danger zone is 5–63°C.

during distribution and on display in shops. Buy food from reputable shops that have refrigerated units for this type of food storage.

Cook food to a high temperature

Bacteria are destroyed at high temperatures, so if food is thoroughly heated to at least 72°C at its centre, for a sufficient time, harmful micro-organisms, including bacteria, will be destroyed. Food can be tested using a food probe to see if a high enough temperature has been reached.

Using a food probe

Use a **food probe** to measure food temperature. Insert the probe to a depth of 2 cm and wait for the temperature to settle. Wipe the probe before and after each use with a bacterial food wipe, to avoid cross-contamination of bacteria from one food to another. Do not push the food probe into frozen food as the probe might snap.

Food businesses have a legal duty to prevent food poisoning by controlling the way they produce, store and handle food. They monitor the temperatures of their food at critical stages during storage, cooking and reheating. The Food Safety Act states that they must not:

- injure the health of consumers
- sell food that is unfit for human consumption
- do anything to the food to make it harmful.

The Act covers food premises including shops and restaurants, and applies to anyone who works in the food industry.

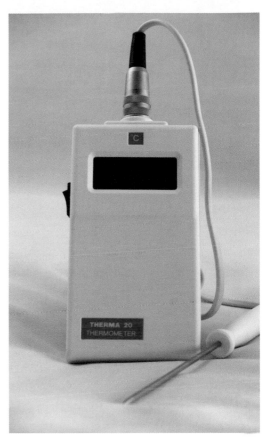
Food probe.

WEBSITES

Foodlink

QUESTIONS

1. What is meant by 'the danger zone'?
2. Why should perishable, high-risk food be kept out of the danger zone?
3. When should a food probe be used by food businesses?
4. How do you avoid cross-contamination when using a food probe?

Temperature: dos and don'ts
- Food should be cooked so that it is hot right through. Salmonella bacteria are killed if they are heated to 72°C and maintained at that heat for two minutes. (This is an example of temperature and time control.)
- When food is kept warm, such as in a self-service canteen, it should be kept warm for as short a time as possible and the food should not be reheated.
- Left-over food should be cooled quickly and kept cool.

Food hygiene and safety

To make sure food is safe to eat, you must store, prepare and cook it hygienically.

Personal hygiene

Hygiene rules to keep the kitchen safe and clean	
Rules	**Reason**
Wear a clean apron or protective clothing when working with food.	This protects the food from the bacteria on your clothes.
Tie back long hair, and remove rings and jewellery.	These all carry bacteria and other contaminants.
Wash your hands before and after working with food and after going to the toilet.	Hands carry bacteria.
If you are ill with diarrhoea or sickness, do not work with food.	The bacteria from these diseases can cause food poisoning.
Do not cough, sneeze or spit near food.	This passes on the bacteria.
Cover any cuts with a plaster.	This prevents bacteria passing on to food.

Wash hands frequently with soap and water throughout food preparation.

Shopping for food

Make sure food is as fresh as possible when it is bought, and store it safely to reduce risks of cross-contamination and deterioration.

Shopping rules for food safety	
Rules	**Reason**
Pack raw foods separately from cooked foods.	This avoids risk of cross-contamination.
Chilled and frozen foods should be packed in a cool bag.	This keeps them at a cold temperature.
Avoid leaving perishable food in warm cars or at room temperature.	The warmth helps bacteria to grow and then the food becomes unsafe.
Check the date mark to make sure the food is in date.	Out-of-date food can be unsafe.
Store food as soon as possible when you get home.	This keeps food as cool as possible.

Storing food

- Food can be stored in the refrigerator, freezer or food cupboard.
- **Ambient temperature** is room temperature. Foods stored at ambient temperatures include canned food, dried food, flour, sugars and biscuits. Keep these away from pests and pets, in a cool, dry place.
- Throw away out-of-date food.
- Store according to the instructions on the packaging.
- Keep food covered.
- Store perishable food in a refrigerator at 5°C or below.
- Store frozen food in a freezer at -18°C or below.
- Cool hot food quickly before storing.
- Keep raw food away from cooked food.

Ambient food is stored at room temperature.

Preparing food

Food needs careful handling and cooking to avoid contamination. Food must be cooked and reheated properly to make sure it reaches a high enough temperature to kill any harmful bacteria that may be present.

Cooking food

Cook food thoroughly. Make sure food is cooked to at least 70°C at the centre – you can test with a food probe. Follow packet instructions, and use suggested cooking temperature and time. Raw chicken contains bacteria, so cook chicken thoroughly.

Reheating food

Cool food quickly if you want to reheat it later. Divide food into small portions and leave in a cold place to cool for up to 90 minutes, then refrigerate or freeze.

Reheat food only once, by cooking to 72°C for at least two minutes. If you are using a microwave, turn and stir the food to avoid cold spots.

KEY TERMS

Ambient temperature room temperature

QUESTIONS

1. Give two rules each for:
   a) good kitchen hygiene
   b) safe shopping for food
   c) storing food.
2. Why should food be heated to 70°C or above?
3. Give two rules for reheating food safely.

Food poisoning 1

Food poisoning is an illness caused by eating food that is contaminated in some way. Up to 5.5 million people a year in the UK are ill from food poisoning.

Pathogenic bacteria

Pathogenic bacteria are those that cause illness. The main sources of food-poisoning bacteria are as follows.

- **People** – bacteria are found in the nose, mouth, intestine and skin, and reach food by poor hygiene, coughing, spitting, cuts on the hands and not washing the hands after going to the toilet.
- **Raw food and soil** – foods that might contain bacteria include raw meat, chicken, eggs and shellfish. Raw food must be stored separately to avoid cross-contamination. Soil from vegetables can contaminate other foods.
- **Pests and pets** – flies, cockroaches, rats, mice and household pets carry food-poisoning bacteria. Keep pets out of the food preparation area.
- **Waste food and rubbish** – bacteria multiply in rotting food and dirty parts of the food preparation area. Clear up waste daily, and wash hands after handling rubbish.

Food poisoning outbreaks

Environmental Health Officers (EHOs) find out the causes of food poisoning outbreaks. People are prosecuted for breaking food hygiene laws, as food poisoning can cause serious illness.

WEBSITES

Food Standards Agency

TO DO

Use the Internet to explore cases of food poisoning outbreaks. Find out the causes and suggest ways the outbreak could be avoided.

KEY TERMS

Pathogenic bacteria are those that cause illness

Cross-contamination when bacteria cross from one food to another

'Kebab shop blamed for food poisoning outbreak'

Ten main causes of food poisoning
1. Food is prepared too early, incorrectly stored at room temperature and not chilled.
2. Cooked food contaminated with food-poisoning bacteria is mixed with other food.
3. Food is cooled too slowly before refrigeration.
4. Food is not reheated to high enough temperatures to destroy food-poisoning bacteria.
5. Undercooked food still contains bacteria.
6. Frozen poultry with bones is not thawed properly.
7. Cross-contamination occurs from raw food to cooked food (see opposite page).
8. Hot food is stored incorrectly below 63°C so that bacteria multiply.
9. Food handlers pass on food poisoning bacteria.
10. Left-overs that are not safe are used.

Cross-contamination of food

Cross-contamination is when bacteria cross from one food to another. This is one of the main causes of food poisoning.

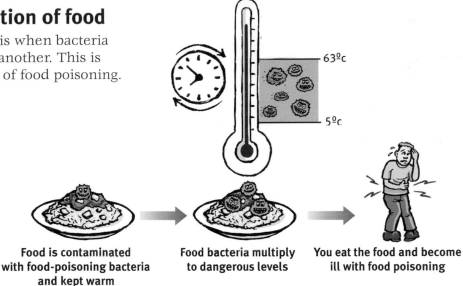

Food is contaminated with food-poisoning bacteria and kept warm → **Food bacteria multiply to dangerous levels** → **You eat the food and become ill with food poisoning**

How food is contaminated with food poisoning bacteria.

Hygiene rules and the reasons for them

Hygiene rule to avoid cross-contamination	Why?
Prepare raw meat and vegetables separately.	To avoid bacteria passing from one to the other.
Wash hands well with soap and water.	To remove bacteria and other organisms that can pass on to food.
Cover all waste and rubbish bins.	To stop flies visiting the bins and then resting on food.
Keep raw and cooked foods apart.	To stop bacteria from raw food passing on to cooked food.
Wash all work surfaces and preparation tools after preparing raw foods.	To stop bacteria from the raw food passing on to other foods.
Use separate equipment for raw and cooked food – including separate chopping boards.	This avoids the risk of raw and cooked foods getting mixed up.
Cover food as soon as it is ready.	This prevents pets and pests getting near the food, and stops cross-contamination.
Make sure cleaning cloths are safe to use by using disposable cloths or disinfecting cloths.	This stops the cloths from passing bacteria around work surfaces.

QUESTIONS

1. Give two reasons why food poisoning is a serious illness.
2. List two of the main causes of food poisoning.
3. List three rules for preparing food that will help to prevent cross-contamination.
4. How would you store food in a refrigerator to prevent cross-contamination?

Food poisoning 2

Campylobacter is the most common cause of food poisoning. Salmonella is the second most common cause, with around 15,000 cases reported each year.

Types of food poisoning bacteria, symptoms, sources and causes

Food-poisoning bacteria	Symptoms	Period before illness starts	Likely sources	Causes
Salmonella	Diarrhoea, vomiting, abdominal pain and fever. Infection may be very severe, and in some cases may be fatal.	12–72 hours	Raw meat, poultry, eggs, raw fresh herbs, raw unwashed vegetables.	Spread by cross-contamination and undercooked food.
Campylobacter	Fever, headache and a feeling of being unwell, followed by severe abdominal pain and diarrhoea, which may be bloody.	2–5 days	Raw poultry and meat, unpasteurised milk, and untreated water.	Cross-contamination can lead to illness. Thorough cooking and pasteurisation of milk will destroy Campylobacter.
Listeria monocytogenes	Symptoms can range from mild flu-like illness to meningitis and septicaemia.	It can take days or weeks for symptoms to develop.	Found in soil, vegetation, raw milk, meat, poultry, cheeses (particularly soft mould-ripened varieties) and salad vegetables.	Thorough cooking of food and pasteurisation of milk will destroy Listeria.
Escheria coli (E coli)	The main symptom is diarrhoea. In the elderly, infection can lead to diarrhoea, which may be severe, kidney failure, and sometimes death.	About 2 days	Underwashed vegetables, infected meat.	Cross-contamination can lead to illness. Thorough cooking of food and pasteurisation of milk will destroy E coli.

(continued)

(continued)

Food-poisoning bacteria	Symptoms	Period before illness starts	Likely sources	Causes
Staphylococcus aureus	Severe vomiting, abdominal pains and diarrhoea. These generally last no longer than 2 days.	2–6 hours	Found on the skin, in infected cuts and boils, and in the nose. Found in cooked meats, poultry and foods that are handled during preparation without further cooking.	Transferred to food from the hands or from droplets from the nose or mouth.
Clostridium prefringens	Symptoms are mainly abdominal pain, diarrhoea and sometimes nausea.	8–18 hours	Found in soil, animal manure, and sewage, and also in raw meat and poultry.	Produces spores that may not be killed during cooking. If foods cool slowly, the spores germinate and produce bacteria which grow rapidly.
Bacillus cereus	Diarrhoea and sometimes vomiting.	1–16 hours	Found in soil and dust. It is found frequently in rice dishes, occasionally in pasta, meat or vegetable dishes.	The bacteria can form spores that are not easily destroyed by heat and will survive cooking of food.

'Listeria scare in chilled food'

QUESTION

Name two types of food-poisoning bacteria and describe:

a) the symptoms of poisoning
b) where the bacteria may be found
c) how they get into food.

ExamCafé

Welcome

Food hygiene and safety

There is a lot to learn in this chapter. The information on food poisoning bacteria is very complicated, so you might need to invent clever ways to remember!

There are a lot of tables in the textbook that you can use for testing yourself.

Revision

Start with a revision plan for all your subjects. Allow enough time to revise for each exam and create a revision diary.

Revise little and often, and give yourself breaks after about an hour's session. This makes your learning more efficient.

Ways to revise

There is no best way to revise. Choose a method that helps you to learn the key facts and knowledge. Some students like to read their classroom notes, others like to make the information simple turning notes into charts and diagrams. Mix up ideas to discover the best way you learn.

Create a revision pack

Make some small revision cards for each section of the specification. These are called prompt cards and provide shortcut answers.

Write down key facts on different sections – writing helps you remember things. You can also sketch, draw and label to explain your ideas.

Test yourself by answering the questions at the end of each double page spread.

Help a partner by testing each other's knowledge.

Work through past question papers.

These are the most useful ways to revise and understand the exam requirements.

- Practise the time it takes to answer the questions.
- Make sure you complete each section and take note of the marks – that is the key to the time you spend on the answers.
- Change methods of revising during a revision session. You could read and test, or get someone to test you.

Some students like to record their revision pack, so they can listen and learn as they walk about.

Websites

BBC GCSE Bitesize (which you can access at www.heinemann.co.uk/hotlinks) has lots of fun ways to revise, but be careful not to waste too much time!

Exemplar questions

Below are some exemplar questions and answers. These questions need longer answers with full sentences and you will need to apply your knowledge for the best marks. The answers show you what the examiners are looking for.

Question 1

This is a buffet that was served to guests at a party. Describe the care needed when preparing and storing this food to keep it safe to eat and not cause food poisoning.

The menu – egg sandwiches, sausage rolls, chicken drumsticks, crème caramel (5 marks).

Answers – any suitable answers will get credit.

There are 5 marks for this answer so make sure you write 5 separate points.

- All the food should be stored at or below 8°C before it is prepared, and after the preparation.
- The refrigerator should be checked to see if it is at the right temperature.
- Food that is cooked, such as the sausage rolls and chicken drumsticks, must be cooked to a core temperature of 72°C.
- Different chopping boards should be used for raw and cooked food.
- Store raw meat such as chicken at the bottom of the fridge.
- Wash hands between preparation of different foods.
- Eggs should be boiled until they are hard, then cooled and kept in chill conditions.
- The crème caramel should be cooked, chilled and stored in chill conditions.

Question 2

What advice would you give for the safe storage of food in a refrigerator? (4 marks)

Answers – any suitable answers will do.

There are 4 marks for this question, so you need 4 points. These are some items.

- Temperature should be between 1°C and 5°C – temperature must be stated.
- Do not overload with food.
- Do not open the door more than needed as it lets warm air in.
- Store raw foods below cooked foods.
- Keep food covered.
- Defrost the fridge regularly and keep clean.
- Do not put hot food into a refrigerator.
- Do not keep food past its sell by date.

Question 3

Discuss three things to consider when buying a refrigerator (4 marks).

Answer – 6 points are needed.

- Check the energy rating to buy one that operates efficiently.
- Choose the size and capacity that meets your needs.
- Choose one that meets your budget needs.
- Look at the storage arrangements in the refrigerator and see if there are enough shelves.
- What additional features are there – automatic defrosting, temperature monitor?
- Is there an ice maker and drinks dispenser?
- Does it open and close easily, and is there a star rating for the freezer section?

Refrigerators and freezers

Refrigerators and freezers help us to keep food safer for longer. Refrigerators keep food cool, and freezers keep food frozen.

WEBSITES

Iceland

Safe use of the refrigerator

The refrigerator should work at between 1°C and 5°C. Check with a refrigerator thermometer. This cold temperature reduces the speed that bacteria grow but does not kill the bacteria.

Rules for safe food storage in a refrigerator	
Rules	**Why?**
Don't overload the refrigerator with food.	Overloading prevents cold air circulating, so the refrigerator does not keep cold.
Don't open the door more than necessary.	This lets in warm air.
Store raw foods below cooked foods to prevent drips.	Prevents cross-contamination from raw to cooked food.
Keep food covered.	This prevents moisture loss and stops cross-contamination.
Keep the refrigerator clean and check that it is working properly.	The temperature can get too high and become dangerous.
Do not place hot food in the refrigerator.	Temperature inside the refrigerator increases dangerously.
Do not keep food beyond its date code.	Chilled food becomes unsafe.

These foods should be kept in the refrigerator.

- Raw meats, fish, poultry, dairy products and eggs.
- Food with a 'use by' date or label that says 'keep refrigerated'.
- Ready-to-eat foods such as salads and desserts.

The freezer

The freezer should work at -18°C or below. Check with a freezer thermometer.

This temperature stops bacterial growth. Frozen food can be kept for some time. Check on the food label for information on storage times.

How does freezing keep food safe?

Freezing turns water to ice and so micro-organisms such as bacteria, yeast and moulds cannot multiply. Once food has been defrosted, it should be treated like fresh food, as the micro-organisms have not been killed.

Keep food cool and covered, and do not put raw food above cooked food.

Rules for safe food storage in a freezer

Rules	Why?
Make sure the freezer is working at -18°C or below.	This temperature stops bacterial growth.
Keep the freezer as full as possible.	Empty freezers use more energy to keep cool.
Wrap food well before freezing to avoid damage to the frozen food and show a 'best before' date.	Food needs protecting from drying out.
Defrost and clean the freezer once every six months.	This helps the freezer to work properly and keep cold.
Never refreeze defrosted food.	Bacteria can multiply to a dangerous level in the thawed food.
Follow the star markings on the packet.	Manufacturers have tested their products for safety.

Star rating symbols found on frozen food compartments

Star rating	Location	Temperature	Storage
*	Ice box	-6 degrees	1 week
**	Ice box	-12 degrees	1 month
***	Ice box	-18 degrees	3 months
****	Freezer	-18 degrees	Long term

*Fast freeze temperature in a **** freezer is -26 degrees.*

STORAGE INSTRUCTIONS

Food freezer† ✳✳✳✳ Until Best
Star marked† ✳✳✳ before date

Frozen food compartment ✳✳ 1 month

Ice-making compartment ✳ 1 week
3 days

Do not re-freeze once thawed

†Should be stored at -18°C or below

Star markings on freezers.

Cook from frozen

One frozen food supermarket says its boned-roast from frozen-joints can go straight from the freezer into the oven, with no need to defrost. These boneless joints guarantee cooking is even and consistent throughout.

Cool bag

When shopping, frozen and chilled food should be put into a cool bag, especially in warm weather. This is insulated to stop the food becoming warm. Food should then be stored in the refrigerator or freezer.

QUESTIONS

1. List five rules for keeping food safely in:
   a) a refrigerator
   b) a freezer.
2. How do the star ratings on a freezer help you to know how long to store frozen food?
3. Why is it important to use a cool bag when buying frozen and chilled food?

Preservation 1

How does **preservation** stop food going bad?

Bacteria, yeast and mould are the micro-organisms that cause changes in food and make it go 'off'.

These micro-organisms need food, warmth, moisture and time to multiply and change.

If these conditions are removed, the food is preserved and will keep for longer.

Enzymes also cause deterioration and these must be destroyed for food to keep.

sugared sprinkles

ice cream (frozen)

cherries in sugar

cream (chilled)

peaches (canned)

raspberry jam

This dessert is made from canned, dried and frozen food.

Different methods of preservation and how they work

Method of preservation	How it works	Examples	Advantages
Drying	Micro-organisms need water to grow and multiply. Drying (dehydration) removes most of the water from food.	Grapes are dried to make sultanas and raisins; fruits such as apricots and figs are dried.	Foods are eaten out of season. They take less space and keep for a long time. Dried foods such as prunes and sultanas have a different taste to the fresh version.
Chilling Chilled food is kept at below 8°C.	At low temperatures, micro-organisms do not multiply as quickly.	Ready meals, salads, sandwiches.	Food tastes like fresh food and has not been changed.
Freezing Home freezers run at -18°C or below and commercial freezers in supermarkets operate at -29°C.	Freezing turns water into ice. Micro-organisms need warmth and liquid to multiply. In freezing, both the warmth and the liquid are removed.	A wide range of fruits, vegetables, ready-prepared meals, cakes and ice cream are frozen.	Frozen food will keep for a very long time.
Canning Food is sealed in a can, liquid added and heated until harmful micro-organisms and spores are killed.	Canned food is heated to a high temperature then sealed so the food is sterile.	Canned vegetables such as tomatoes, fruit such as peaches, soups, stews and puddings.	Can be kept in ambient conditions and lasts a long time.

(continued)

(continued)

Method of preservation	How it works	Examples	Advantages
Chemicals **Salt** (sodium chloride) is used to salt meat and fish **Sugar** is used for jams which is a way to preserve fruits **Vinegar** is used for pickles and chutneys to preserve vegetables **Alcohol** is used for fruits such as peaches in brandy **Smoke** preserves fish and meat **Spices** preserve meats, e.g. salami	Chemicals remove the available water from food so that micro-organisms cannot multiply. A range of chemicals is used as preservatives for food products. They protect food against micro-organisms and increase the shelf life of food products.	Salted fish, bacon, jams, pickles, smoked fish.	Increases the shelf life of products but changes the taste and flavour and texture.
Vacuum packing	Oxygen is removed from the packaging so micro-organisms cannot grow.	Used for cold meats, cheese, bacon, fish.	Food tastes very fresh yet will keep for a long time.
Modified atmosphere packaging (MAP)	The gas content within the packaging is changed, which slows the growth of bacteria and micro-organisms.	Used for ready washed salads and vegetables.	Food tastes very fresh and lasts longer.

QUESTIONS

1. Name the three micro-organisms that make food go bad.
2. Give two reasons why food needs to be preserved.
3. Name two methods of preservation, then:
   a) explain how they preserve foods
   b) give two examples in each case.

KEY TERMS

Preservation stopping food going bad

Enzymes chemicals that cause changes in food

Yeast a micro-organism that changes food

Preservation 2

Ways to preserve foods at home

- **Pickling** – such as pickled vegetables and onions. The ingredients are stored in vinegar and keep for some time, as the vinegar prevents growth of micro-organisms.
- **Jamming** – for fruits such as strawberries and blackcurrants. Plenty of heat and sugar is used in jamming, which prevents deterioration.
- **Bottling** – fruit and vegetables are heated in liquids in glass jars and then sealed.
- **Making chutney** – vegetables and fruits such as apples, mangoes and limes can be preserved by adding salt, sugar and vinegar.

Manufacturers preserve foods to help extend the **shelf life**.

Commercial methods of preservation

Accelerated Freeze Drying (AFD)

For this process, food is frozen and dried under vacuum. The ice changes to water vapour without passing through the liquid stage, leaving the food dry. This process preserves the flavour and colour of the food. It is used for soups and instant coffee granules.

Cryogenic freezing or immersion freezing

Food such as prawns or soft fruits is immersed or sprayed with liquid nitrogen. The food is frozen immediately, but this is an expensive process.

Fast freezing is best. Slow freezing breaks down the walls of the food and changes its appearance. Strawberries become mushy if they are frozen too slowly.

High Temperature Short Time Canning (HTST)

Very high temperatures reduce processing time and prevent food from becoming over-processed and losing texture.

Pasteurisation

Heat treatment lengthens shelf life and makes a product safer to eat. For milk, pasteurisation involves heating to 72°C, holding for at least 15 seconds and cooling rapidly to 10°C. Pasteurisation destroys many but not all of the micro-organisms present. Other products that can be pasteurised include orange juice.

Food can be preserved at home by pickling, jamming, bottling and making into chutneys.

KEY TERMS

Shelf life the length of time a food will keep

Accelerated Freeze Drying (AFD) where food is frozen and dried under vacuum

Cryogenic freezing or **immersion** freezing when food is immersed or sprayed with liquid nitrogen

Irradiated food food bombarded with ionising rays

UHT (Ultra Heat Treatment)

This process is used for milk and destroys all bacteria. Milk is heated to 132°C–140°C for up to 5 seconds and cooled quickly. This makes the milk sterile but alters the taste. UHT milk will keep for several months without refrigeration.

Irradiation

Food is irradiated by bombarding it with ionising radiation to make it keep longer. By law irradiated food must be labelled, but it is not sold in the UK at the moment.

WEBSITES

HowStuffWorks

Advantages of irradiation	Disadvantages of irradiation
Eliminates harmful bacteria. Kills pests and parasites. Prevents vegetables from sprouting and fruits from ripening.	Vitamins are lost during processing. Toxins can remain in food. Old food can be cleaned up and sold as fresh. There is no test to find if foods have been irradiated.

Changes in nutrition during preservation

Process	Changes in nutrition
Drying	Dried foods have a higher energy value than fresh foods because of the loss of water. Vitamin C is lost during drying.
Freezing	The nutritional loss is very small. Blanching causes some loss of the water-soluble vitamins C and thiamin but the final cooking time is reduced, so frozen vegetables can be just as nutritious as fresh. Many frozen vegetables are more nutritious than fresh, since they are frozen very quickly after harvesting.
Canning	Some loss of nutrients occurs during heating – thiamin is lost from meat and vitamin C from fruit and vegetables. Canned foods are nearly as good as fresh foods in nutritional value. Fruit and vegetables are canned within hours of picking, so few nutrients are lost.

QUESTIONS

1. Name one method of home preservation and explain why it helps the food to keep longer.
2. Name one method of commercial preservation and explain why it helps the food to keep longer.
3. What nutrients might be lost during the following:
   a) drying
   b) freezing
   c) canning?

Food labelling 1

A food label can provide you with lots of useful information. Food labels must follow the Food Labelling Regulations and give the following details:

- name and description of the food
- list of ingredients in weight descending order
- date code
- special conditions of storage or use
- weight/volume in the pack
- place of origin, if relevant
- name and address of manufacturer, packer or EC seller
- any special preparation or cooking instructions.

WEBSITES

Food Standards Agency

List of ingredients

The largest amount of ingredient by weight is listed first, so in an autumn berry cobbler, for example (see opposite), the autumn berry filling is the heaviest part (64 per cent). Manufacturers must state what additives are used – for example, in the cobbler, *raising agent: disphosphates, colour beta-carotene.*

Date codes

'Best before' dates are used on products that keep for a while. These products won't go bad but after that date their quality may have deteriorated. 'Use by' dates are important and mean that the food will go off, so it must be used before that time.

Storage instructions

These tell you how to store the food and whether it should be kept in the fridge and/or the freezer.

Name and address of the maker, packer or retailer and place of origin

Nutritional information

This is optional unless a nutrition claim such as 'low fat' or 'reduced salt' is made. The values are given per 100 g and many products give information per portion. This will show how many calories, how much protein, fat and carbohydrate there is in the product. Some products show the amount of saturated fat, sugar, fibre and sodium (or salt) and compare this to Guideline Daily Amounts.

Autumn berry cobbler

Ingredients

Autumn berry filling (64%), scones (36%)

Autumn berry filling – Bramley apples (52%), blackcurrants (10%), raspberries (10%), sugar, water, maize starch.

Scones – wheat flour, butter, milk, egg, sugar, glucose syrup, raising agent diphosphates, salt, colour betacarotene.

1 of your 5 a day fruit and vegetables.

How to store and cook

Use by 17 December 2010
Keep refrigerated below 5°C
Do not exceed the use by date

Oven cook from chilled electric 190°C, Gas 5 for 18–20 mins.

Allergy advice

Contains egg, gluten and milk. May contain traces of nuts and sesame.

Net weight 595 grams
Ⓥ Vegetarian

123456   01.01
0000 0000   Z1234

Made by Jenny's Bakery, Kettering, Northants

Nutrition information	Per 100 g	per ¼ cobbler
Energy	834 kJ 198 kcal	1248 kJ 296 kcal
Protein	3 g	4.5 g
Carbohydrate	34 g	51 g
of which sugars	15.6 g	23.4 g
Fat	5.3 g	7.9 g
of which saturates	3.8 g	5.7 g
Fibre	2 g	3 g
Salt	0.6 g	0.88 g

Autumn berry cobbler.

QUESTIONS

Use the autumn berry cobbler label to answer these questions.

1. Name two ingredients that provide:
   a) fibre
   b) sugar.
2. Name three allergens in this food.
3. Name three ingredients that help this cobbler claim to be one of your five a day.
4. How should the cobbler be stored and cooked?
5. What additives are used in the cobbler?

Food labelling 2

Nutrition labelling

This is only needed by law when a nutrition or health claim is made, or vitamins or minerals are added to food. Most labels show nutritional value as this helps consumers make healthy choices.

Date codes

Food labels have date codes to show how old the food is.

- **'Use by'** dates are shown on food with a short shelf life, which should be stored in a refrigerator.
- **'Best before'** date codes are on foods with short to medium shelf life, such as biscuits.
- 'Display until' date codes are used by the store to tell them when to remove the product.

'Use by' and 'best before' dates.

Allergen information

Labelling requires 14 allergen ingredients to be shown on pre-packed foods. These allergen foods are as follows:

1. celery, 2. cereals containing gluten (wheat, barley, rye and oats), 3. crustaceans (such as lobster and crab), 4. eggs, 5. fish, 6. lupin, 7. milk, 8. molluscs (such as mussels and oysters), 9. mustard, 10. nuts – almonds, hazelnuts, walnuts, Brazil nuts, cashews, pecans, 11. peanuts, 12. sesame seeds, 13. soya beans and soya products, 14. sulphur dioxide and sulphites (preservatives used in foods and drinks).

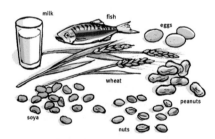

Foods that can cause allergies.

Bar codes

This symbol helps to identify goods using a computer. Each bar code is unique and read by optical character recognition equipment. Bar codes make shop checkouts quick and easy, and give information on receipts. Bar codes help with stock control and supply of goods.

Quantitative Ingredient Declaration (QUID)

The quantity of an ingredient used in a food product is shown as a percentage. This information is useful when comparing products like the following three apple pies.

- Apple pie – apple filling 53%, pastry 51%
- Apple pie basics – apple filling 44%, pastry 53%
- Apple pie Taste the difference – apple filling 58%, pastry 40%.

Bar codes give detailed information.

Guideline Daily Amounts

Guideline Daily Amounts (GDAs) on food labels help you plan a healthy balanced diet. Each GDA is for an average adult. They are called guidelines because they are a guide, not a target. The GDA label has five parts – calories, sugars, fat, saturates and salt.

Traffic light system

The **traffic light system** shows if the food is high, medium or low in fat, saturated fat, sugars and salt. Green means low in one of the nutrients, amber means medium, and red means high in a nutrient. This helps you to make healthy choices.

Limits for the traffic light labeling

‹ means less than	≤ means less than or equal to	› means more than	
	Green (low)	**Amber (medium)**	**Red (high)**	
Fat	≤ 3.0 g/100 g	› 3.0 to ≤ 20.0 g/100 g	› 20.0 g/100 g	› 21.0 g/portion
Saturates	≤ 1.5 g/100 g	› 1.5 to ≤ 5.0 g/100 g	› 5.0 g/100 g	› 6.0 g/portion
Total sugars	≤ 5.0 g/100 g	› 5.0 to ≤ 15.0 g/100 g	› 15.0 g/100g	› 18.0 g/portion
Salt	≤ 0.30 g/100 g	› 0.30 to ≤ 1.50g/100 g	› 1.50 g/100 g	› 2.40 g/portion

Special dietary needs

Labels show if the product:

- is suitable for vegetarians
- is gluten free
- contains peanuts.

This helps people who need to make special food choices. Additive statements can show if the food contains no added colour, preservatives or artificial flavours.

Mince pie

Iced bun

Traffic light system.

1. Explain what is meant by the following terms:
   a) date codes
   b) allergens
   c) bar codes.
2. What is meant by Guideline Daily Amounts?
3. Describe the traffic light system and explain why it is useful on a food label.

Food packaging

Food needs to be packaged to keep it safe and to provide us with information.

Functions of food packaging

- Reduces food waste by protecting food from damage – eggs in cartons.
- Increases the life of food – putting food in a can or changing the gas inside the packaging.
- Gives information on the contents and shelf life.
- Makes food easier to handle, transport and store.
- Improves hygiene, since food cannot be touched by hand.

Modified atmosphere packaging (MAP)

Food manufacturers can change the types of gas inside packaging to increase the shelf life of the product. **Modified atmosphere packaging (MAP)** replaces most of the oxygen in the packs with carbon dioxide and nitrogen gas. This is used in ready-prepared salads, minced meat and bacon. The food looks, tastes and smells just like fresh food, but the change of gas slows the growth of micro-organisms.

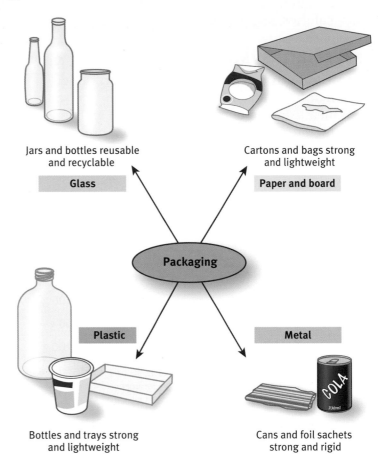

Jars and bottles reusable and recyclable

Glass

Cartons and bags strong and lightweight

Paper and board

Packaging

Plastic

Bottles and trays strong and lightweight

Metal

Cans and foil sachets strong and rigid

Packaging is made from paper, metal, glass and plastic.

Packaging materials	
Packaging	**Used for**
Paper and board	Cartons, paper bags, juice cartons
Plastic	Bottles, trays, squeezy bottles
Metal – aluminium and steel	Cans, foil trays and foil covers
Glass	Glass jars and bottles

Types of food packaging

Different types of packaging and how they are used

Packaging	Advantages	Disadvantages
Paper and board	Strong and lightweight, does not break easily, can be printed, can be recycled.	Does not protect food from damp, crushes easily. Recycled paper and card cannot be used with food products.
Plastic	Strong and lightweight, good barrier to moisture, can be printed, does not react to foods, can be recycled.	A litter problem, as it does not biodegrade easily.
Metal – aluminium and steel	Strong and rigid, good barrier to water and gas, can be printed easily.	Must be coated on the inside, otherwise it reacts to the product.
Glass	Reusable and easily recycled, good barrier to water, transparent, can be printed.	Easily broken.

Vacuum packing

This process removes all the air from the pack and keeps food with no oxygen, which increases the shelf life. Once the packs are opened, they have a normal shelf life.

Tamper-proof packaging

Shrink-wrapped jars and plastic collars on bottles are types of tamper-proof packaging. They show that the pack has not been opened and the contents have not been changed or damaged. This helps with product safety.

Biodegradable packaging

Biodegradable packaging can be broken down by other living organisms, and the packaging does not need to go to landfill. Manufacturers and supermarkets are increasingly using more biodegradable packaging.

- **Degradable** plastic is made from oil with additives to help it break down to carbon dioxide and water. The process takes two years to complete.
- **Compostable** or **biodegradable plastic** is usually made from plant-based starch that breaks down into carbon dioxide and water.
- **Polylactic acid (PLA)**, made from plants such as corn, is used for packaging for punnets or pallets. It is used for packaging film, bottles and labels. It takes about nine weeks to biodegrade if factors like temperature are right.

KEY TERMS

Modified atmosphere packaging (MAP) packaging where the oxygen in packs is replaced to prolong shelf life

Biodegradable packaging packaging that can be broken down by other living organisms

Polylactic acid a chemical used for biodegradable packaging

QUESTIONS

1. Give three reasons why food packaging is important.
2. What is mean by MAP and vacuum packing?
3. Why is tamper-proof packaging needed? Give one example of its use.
4. What is meant by biodegradable packaging?

Recycling food packaging

Nearly 25 per cent of our rubbish is made up of packaging – the pie chart below shows the percentage of the different materials that are used. Recycling is good for the environment; material not put out for recycling will go to landfill, so people must recycle as many things as possible.

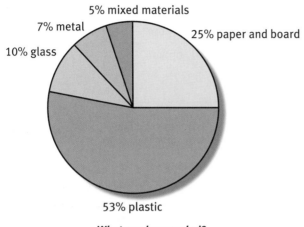

5% mixed materials

7% metal

10% glass

25% paper and board

53% plastic

What can be recycled?

WEBSITES

Waste Online

Wrap

Reducing the amount of packaging

Manufacturers try to use less packaging for food products and should use only what is essential. Shoppers can reuse containers and recycle bottles at bottle banks. To lower the amount of food packaging we should reduce, reuse and recycle.

Packaging materials

How easy is it to recycle the different types of packaging?		
Packaging	**Advantages**	**Disadvantages**
Paper and board	Renewable resource that can be recycled.	If food comes into contact with the packaging, it cannot be recycled.
Plastic	Strong and lightweight and some can be recycled; if recycled, less oil is used for plastic production.	Needs sorting into different types if it is to be recycled, which is difficult.
Metal – aluminium and steel	Steel is separated from aluminium using magnets and both can be recycled; high value as scrap metals.	A lot of energy is used in extraction.
Glass	Reusable and easily recycled.	Brittle and dangerous to handle.

- **Reduce:** Buy less packaging and avoid over-packaged products. Avoid taking too many plastic bags when packing shopping.
- **Reuse:** Some toiletries and cleaning liquids are sold in refillable or returnable containers, and some milk in returnable glass bottles. It is not safe to reuse materials that have been near food, but you can reuse plastic shopping bags.
- **Recycle:** Many packaging materials can be collected for recycling, such as paper, glass and plastic bottles.

Recycling symbols found on packaging

Mobius loop Shows that the packaging can be recycled. 	**Mobius loop with percentage** Shows the amount of the packaging that can be recycled.	**Recyclable glass** Shows the product can be taken to a bottle bank. 
Recyclable steel Shows the product is made from steel that could be recycled.  RECYCLABLE STEEL	**Recyclable aluminium** Shows the product is made from aluminium that can be recycled.	**Tidyman symbol** Used to encourage people to recycle and put things in bins.
Green dot Means that the manufacturer has paid a fee towards the packaging recovery system in Germany.	**PET** Used for fizzy drinks, mineral water, squashes, cooking oils.  PET	**High density polyethylene** Used for milk and juice bottles, washing up liquid and shower bottles.  HDPE  HDPE

1. Give three reasons why it is important to recycle food packaging.
2. Name three types of materials that can be recycled.
3. Explain how you could persuade shoppers to reduce the amount of packaging they buy.

ExamCafé

Welcome

Food packaging and labels can help you learn a lot about the ingredients, nutrition and types of packaging used for food products.

Make a large collection and share them with your group. You can scan the label and use it for revision, or you can type it out like the example shown. Then make up some questions to ask about the product and pass them around the group.

This is the best way to learn things – using real examples of foods, which provide up-to-date information.

Here is an example of how you could use a label to help revise.

Light and fruity bread and butter pudding

Description: slices of bread (8%), butter (0.5%), set in an egg (21%) custard made with whipping cream (31%) scattered with sultanas (4.5%) and nutmeg.

Serving size: half a pudding 197g

Ingredients: custard, bread, sultanas, butter, nutmeg
Custard contains: whipping cream, milk, pasteurised egg, sugar, flavouring, colour (beta carotene).
Bread contains: wheat flour, water, yeast, salt, soya flour, vinegar, vegetable oil.
Made by Toscas Food Company, Anytown, UK.

Nutrition

	100 g	Half a pudding	GDA	GDA %
Energy	1035 kJ	2045 kJ	2000 kcal	25%
	250 kcal	490 kcal		
Protein	5 g	9.9 g		
Carbohydrate	20.8 g	41.1 g		
of which sugars	17 g	33.6 g	90 g	37%
Fat	16.1 g	31.8 g	70 g	45%
of which saturates	9.7 g	19.1 g	20 g	96%
Fibre	0.4 g	0.8 g		
Sodium	0.1 g	0.2 g		
Salt equivalent	0.2 g	0.5 g	6 g	8%

Cooking

Oven 30 minutes 180°C/Gas Mark 4
- Remove outer packaging, place on a baking tray in the centre of a preheated oven for 30 minutes.

Microwave
- Remove outer packaging.
- Heat on full power for 2 ½ minutes. Turn, then heat on full power for a further 2 ½ minutes (total time 5 minutes).
- Check food is piping hot throughout before serving.

Freezing instructions: Freeze on day of purchase. Use within one month. Defrost thoroughly for a minimum of 6 hours in the refrigerator. If the food is thawed, do not refreeze.

Storage: Keep refrigerated. Use by – see the front of the pack.

Allergy advice: Contains milk, wheat, gluten, egg, soya. Cannot guarantee nut free.

V – Suitable for vegetarians.

Weight: 395G e

Packaging information: PET tray which can be recycled, cardboard carton which can be recycled.

Use by date: 15 Jan 2009

Claims: No artificial preservatives, flavours or colours.

Here are some questions you could ask about this product.

1. What are the main ingredients used in this product?
2. How could the product be changed to lower:
   a) the fat
   b) the sugar?
3. How could you increase the amount of fibre in this product?
4. The nutrition analysis shows that it is high in fat, saturated fat and sugar. How much of the GDA does a portion supply?
5. How much of the GDA for energy does one portion supply? Give your views on this.
6. What is the allergy advice for this product?
7. When cooking the product, why does the outer packaging have to be removed?
8. When cooking in the microwave, why does the product have to be turned halfway through the cooking process?
9. Why should the food be frozen on the day of purchase?
10. How should the product be stored and how do you know when it should be used?
11. What claims are made about this product?
12. How can the packaging be recycled?

Now make your own collection of labels and complete the following details for each one:
- name of product
- manufacturer's address
- description
- serving size
- ingredients
- nutrition with traffic lights or GDAs
- traffic light colours
- cooking instructions
- freezing instructions
- storage
- allergy advice
- suitability for vegetarians
- packaging information
- weight
- use-by or best-before date
- claims.

Advertising and marketing research

What is advertising?

Consumers are people who buy and use things. **Advertising** provides information about products and services and gives consumers reasons to buy things. New products must be advertised so that people know they are available. Advertisements target the group most likely to buy the product and give them the information they need.

The biggest spenders on food and drink advertisements are supermarkets and manufacturers of chocolate, crisps, snacks and sweets. Children are important when making decisions about family food and advertisers create ways to attract them to their products. This is known as **pester power**.

There are many different ways to advertise and promote products, including: TV, radio and cinema advertisements, the Internet, newspapers and magazines, posters, competitions and leaflets posted to homes.

Complaints about advertising

The rules about advertising are administered by the Advertising Standards Authority (ASA), and it is their job to investigate and respond to complaints about advertising. Visit their website to submit a complaint. In the case of advertising on television and radio, the ASA are acting on behalf of Ofcom, the communications regulator, who have put in place tough rules to control broadcast advertising to children of foods high in fats, salt and sugar.

For complaints about written adverts, the Advertising Standards Authority (**ASA**) is the organisation to contact.

Ofcom regulates the UK's broadcasting sector.

This independent body oversees the codes of practice drawn up by the advertising industry. Adverts must be legal, decent, honest and truthful.

Your local Trading Standards Department also deals with complaints.

WEBSITES

Advertising Standards Authority

Ofcom

Marketing

Market research

Market research helps plan how to promote and advertise a product. Different types of market research include:

- **direct (primary) research** – getting information using the telephone, interviews, tasting sessions and questionnaires
- **secondary research** – using existing information found on the Internet and in research reports.

Research can be:

- **quantitative** – using questionnaires and interviews
- **qualitative** – asking people for their views and opinions.

How do supermarkets persuade people to buy products?

Companies pay supermarkets to place their products in popular areas of the shop. This is called product placement, and it helps to increase sales and make people aware of the product. Eye level is buy level – this is the most popular shelf position for people to buy from.

Special offers include money off, buy one get one free (BOGOF), three for two, 30 per cent extra, gifts with the product and competitions to enter. These all encourage people to buy. Loyalty cards give shoppers money off and vouchers.

Snack food for teenagers

When a new food product is developed for sale, the team needs to consider:

- **who** will buy it – what sort of teenagers is it aimed at? Boys or girls? Younger or older? Where do they live? Do they have their own income, or is someone else going to be buying this for them?
- **why** they will buy it – is it attractive, cheap, convenient, the latest fashion?
- **when** they will buy it – a snack food is bought by busy people on the move
- **where** they will buy it – what kinds of shops will sell the product?

QUESTIONS

1. Describe the work of Ofcom and ASA, and explain how their work is useful.
2. Make a list of the different ways of advertising a product. Give the advantages and disadvantages of the different ways.
3. What is the difference between direct (primary) research and secondary research?
4. What is the advantage to shoppers of the following methods of food promotion?
   a) buy one get one free
   b) a sample to try
   c) a money-off voucher.

Household and shopping trends

Surveys

The National Food Survey was set up in the 1940s to investigate the UK diet during the war years. It is now called the **Expenditure and Food Survey** and collects data on food consumption and expenditure. These are some results from recent surveys.

- The UK is buying more healthy foods such as fruit and vegetables, fish and high fibre breakfast cereals.
- The UK diet is still too high in fat, saturated fat and non-milk extrinsic sugars.
- We spend more money on eating out than buying food to eat at home.

The graph on the right shows the changes in the types of food that people are buying.

Changing trends

Trends in the home kitchen

Homes are getting smaller, with less space for storing and cooking food. Fridges and freezers may only hold enough food for a few meals. In the past, big chest freezers stored frozen food from family gardens and food stores.

At the same time, many people now use the microwave oven to reheat ready-prepared meals and snacks. People make less use of cooking equipment, so the meals that we choose are changing. There have been huge developments in ready-prepared food for family meals such as ready meals, frozen dinners and takeaway food and this changes the way we live and eat.

Trends in families

The number of family households with two parents and two children is declining. The number of single parents living with their dependant children is growing. There is a large increase in people living alone and people are living longer.

Men, women and children often share the task of cooking the family meal. In the past many women stayed at home and took care of the shopping and household tasks, but now more women go out to work. Family members may work at nights, or be busy with activities, so not all the family eat meals together in the evenings and at weekends.

There is more fast food available to buy and eat quickly on the streets. Hot food like pizzas or Chinese meals can be delivered to the home.

People eat more snacks and so do not sit down to meals as they used to years ago.

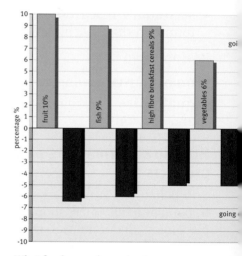

What foods people are buying.

Ready meals are now more popular than ever b

Shopping for food

- Supermarkets supply a huge range of food products along with other goods. They often have their own range of food products, which includes budget ranges with simple packaging and lower prices to help people save money.
- Some towns still have local butchers, greengrocers, bakers and fishmongers. The food can be fresher and sold at a good price.
- Corner shops are famous for opening for long hours, seven days a week. They sell a range of fresh, canned and frozen food and are handy for people who do not want to travel long distances for their shopping.
- Street markets and farmers' markets offer good value for shoppers, as the food is fresh and often sold at a lower price.
- Some businesses visit their local area and sell meat, fish and cheeses. Some mail order companies will pack and send goods to your home.

Shopping online

The Internet is responsible for one of the greatest changes in the way we shop for food and other goods. You can order online and the goods are delivered to your home. The advantages of shopping this way are that it saves time, travel and parking costs, and you can compare the costs on different websites. Disadvantages are that you do not see the goods before you buy, you have to return the goods if they are not suitable, and if goods are not in stock, they will not be delivered.

TO DO

Create a PowerPoint® presentation to show the advantages and disadvantages of the different places to shop for food.

Food can be delivered to the home.

QUESTIONS

1. What types of food are we buying more of and less of?
2. How will these changes improve the quality of our diet?
3. Suggest three reasons why people are choosing to eat food away from home.
4. Give the advantages and disadvantages of shopping for food in different places. Copy and complete this table to help you.

Type of shop	Advantages	Disadvantages
Supermarket		
Small shop		
Street market		
Online shopping		

Ethical shopping

Here are some **ethical** issues to consider when we shop for food.

Who produces the food I buy?

Farmers' markets

Farmers' markets are often held out of doors and aim to sell locally produced food. In the UK, the National Farmers' Retail Markets Association has a code of conduct with guidelines for farmers' markets:

- Food must come from a local area.
- The food must be sold by someone involved in producing it.
- Primary products – fruit, vegetables, meat – must be grown locally.
- Secondary products such as bread, pickles and chutneys must contain a local ingredient.
- All food must be traceable.

Other farmers' outlets

Farmers and producers also sell their food products through farm shops, box schemes and home deliveries. Box schemes deliver boxes of locally produced fruits and vegetables, or packs of meat to people's homes.

Fairtrade

Fairtrade products aim to give farmers in developing countries a better deal. The Fairtrade Foundation certifies

WEBSITES

Fairtrade

KEY TERMS

Ethical to do with morals, whether something is right or wrong

Farmers market a local market that sells locally produced food

Fairtrade trade that aims to give producers a fair price for what they grow or make, and to help them improve their working conditions

Food miles the distance food travels from source to plate

Buying at farmers' markets has become very popular.

products from farmers in developing countries and makes sure the farmers get a good price – enough to provide a steady income and cover the costs of sustainable production. The FAIRTRADE Mark is found on thousands of products, including tea, chocolate, cotton and coffee. Fairtrade bananas are bestsellers, but Fairtrade products make up a tiny percentage of what we buy. Fairtrade products are usually no more expensive than others.

The FAIRTRADE Mark.

How far has my food travelled?
Food miles

Food miles tell us the distance our food travels 'from field to plate': this is the journey from where food is grown or produced to the consumer. Food miles make us aware of the environmental impact of transporting foods around the world, but working out the full impact is not a simple matter.

For example, in wintertime, it is better for the environment to transport tomatoes from Spain than to grow them in the UK. In Spain, tomatoes are grown outside under plastic sheeting; in the UK, energy is needed to heat the greenhouses where tomatoes grow in wintertime – so in this case it is better to import the tomatoes from a hotter country.

What is the impact of my food on the environment?
Carbon footprints of food products

A carbon footprint measures our impact on the environment by looking at the greenhouse gases produced from electricity, transport and heating. Greenhouse gases are found in the atmosphere and help protect the temperature of the earth. A product's 'lifecycle' is analysed to work out its carbon footprint, from the raw materials through to packaging, distribution and disposal of packaging. The aim is to help businesses develop new products with lower carbon footprints.

INVESTIGATION

Investigate the range of Fairtrade products that are available to use in cooking. Create a dish using one of these products.

TO DO

Create a product that is made mostly from locally sourced ingredients. Use the Internet to help with this research.

The carbon footprint logo.

QUESTIONS

1. Explain what is meant by the following terms: farmers' markets, food miles, Fairtrade.
2. What are the five guidelines for people running a stall at a farmers' market?
3. Give the advantages and disadvantages of buying food that is locally produced.

Food production and sustainability

In the 21st century, farming has to be environmentally responsible, but it also has to produce affordable, wholesome food. The British Isles are small and densely populated, and our agriculture produces only 60 per cent of our food needs. The extra food is imported from other countries.

A **sustainable** system is one that 'meets the needs of the present without compromising the ability of future generations to meet their own needs'. Traditional farming methods are sustained by the use of good farming practices and more recently non organic farmers have relied on the use of pesticides and artificial fertilisers. Organic farming can be considered sustainable, as it reuses resources and maintains the environment. Organic farmers use techniques such as crop rotations to make the soil more fertile and reduce pests.

New research suggests that if England and Wales were to farm organically we could feed the population with changes to our diet, including eating less meat. The consequence of this would be that, as a nation, we would enjoy a far healthier diet and animal welfare would be improved considerably.

What is organic food?

Organic food is produced as naturally as possible, free from trans fats, **GM** food and most additives. Food labelled as 'organic' meets strict standards for the use of pesticides, additives, animal welfare and sustainability. Organic farms use few chemicals and most pesticides are banned. To get an organic certificate, animals must have access to outdoor, organic land, and the numbers are controlled. Chickens are free range, able to scratch about outdoors and get plenty of sunlight.

In the UK, the Soil Association and Organic Farmers & Growers are the main organisations that check on farms and food products to make sure they meet the standards.

There are lots of reasons to eat organic food. There is a growing body of research that shows organic food can be more nutritious for you and many people also think it tastes better. Organic food contains more of the good stuff we need – like vitamins and minerals – and less of the bad stuff that we don't – pesticides, additives and drugs.

FACT

Global food prices are rising and the world population is increasing. One billion people do not get enough to eat.

Organic food is labelled.

WEBSITES

Soil Association

Organic Farmers and Growers

Organic Certification UK2

These are the main organisations that check on organic food standards.

Organic food may cost more because food production is more labour intensive than in other farming, crops are grown less often in the same piece of ground and animals are held at lower stocking densities. However, it depends on how and what you buy. If you buy seasonal food from direct sources, such as your local farmers' market or nearest vegetable box scheme, organic food can be cheaper.

What is genetically modified food (GM food)?

Pro-GM lobbyists say genetically modified crops have the potential to be more nutritious, resistant to drought and disease, and to grow without chemical fertilisers. However, GM crops do not currently live up to these claims and many supermarkets stopped selling them due to pressure from consumers. Those opposed to GM crops generally believe that any overall assessment of the list of risks indicates that GM crops cannot be proved to be safe to be used for animal feed or food. Some European governments, however, have been persuaded to allow GM crops to be grown as long as there is a 'case by case' risk assessment. There are no GM crops currently being grown commercially in the UK.

The first GM food sold in the UK was tomato paste. New GM products include:

- GM maize grown in the USA
- GM soya with fish oils.

Some GM medicines already exist – for example, human insulin produced by bacteria.

Food waste

We waste more than £10 billion worth of food in the UK each year. Most food waste goes to landfill. More than 15p of each £1 spent on food is wasted. One-fifth of our carbon emissions are created by the production, processing, transport and storage of food so, to be more environmentally friendly, we must reduce food waste. As well as cooking the right amounts, eating everything up and using left-overs creatively, you could compost vegetable and fruit peelings by making a compost heap in the garden.

Biodigester

A **biodigester** can dispose of food waste. Ludlow is the first town in the UK to collect household food waste and put it into a biodigester to produce electricity and biofertiliser. The householders throw away an average of 2.5 kilos of collected food waste a week that would otherwise go to landfill.

KEY TERMS

Sustainable being able to keep something going for some time

Genetically modified food food grown from or using plants that have been genetically changed in some way

Biodigester a machine that changes food waste into electricity and biofertiliser

INVESTIGATION

1. Find out how much food a week is wasted in your household. Keep a record of the food cost and how much the waste weighed. How could you could reduce the amount of food waste in your household and how much money could you save?

2. Do some research on the Internet to find out about the issues of GM food crops. What are your views on using GM foods in the future?

QUESTIONS

1. What do the terms 'sustainable', 'organic' and 'GM' mean?
2. Why do you think people choose to buy organic food?
3. Give the advantages and disadvantages of buying organic food.

Ethical food labels

People are concerned about factory farming, global warming, fair trading and environmental issues. Food products carry an increasing number of labels which help us make ethical choices. For example, many people want to buy organic fruit and vegetables or bananas that have been grown by people earning a fair wage.

Vegetarian SOCIETY

TO DO

Visit some of the websites that show these ethical food labels and find out more about what they do. Find out about the advantages of using these labels on food products.

Red Tractor

The crossed grain symbol

Organic Certification UK2

Food labels that help us make ethical choices.

Some symbols you will find on food products to help make choices

Soil Association – organic food	The Soil Association is the main organisation in the UK that checks on farms and food products to make sure they meet organic standards. The Soil Association is also the UK's leading environmental charity promoting sustainable, organic farming and championing human health.
Organic Farmers & Growers	This is another UK organisation that certifies that the food is produced organically.
European symbol for organic food	The European Union has introduced a new logo for organic food. The new logo is now obligatory for all organic products sold within the European Union member states.
GM free	This shows that the product does not contain genetically modified ingredients. The Soil Association and the Vegetarian Society do not approve food with GM ingredients.
The Vegetarian Society – vegetarian food	Many food companies label their food as suitable for vegetarians. There are many symbols, but the most popular ones are used by the Vegetarian Society and the Vegan Society. The Vegetarian Society will label food that does not contain animal flesh or products, such as gelatine, which is made from animal products.
Vegan Society	Food products must be free from any animal products. The Vegan Society trademark logo is used on products which are free of animal involvement and have been registered with the Vegan Society.
Fairtrade	The Fairtrade Foundation makes sure that farmers in developing countries get a good price for their products and are treated fairly.
Carbon footprint	The carbon footprint shows that the company has analysed a product's lifecycle to work out its carbon footprint and impact on the environment.
Leaf Marque	This helps you to choose products that are produced by farmers who want to improve the environment.
Freedom Food	RSPCA Welfare Standards is the only farm assurance and food labelling scheme dedicated to improving the lives of farm animals. Freedom Food inspect farms to ensure they meet strict welfare standards covering all aspects of lives, including living conditions, handling and transport.
Red Tractor	The Red Tractor is an independent mark of quality that guarantees the food we buy comes from farms and food companies that meet high standards of food safety and hygiene, animal welfare and environmental protection.

QUESTION

Explain why you think people might be concerned about three of these ethical issues when buying food.

Cost of food

Food prices will increase as global prices.

What makes the price of food rise?

- Increases in fuel costs.
- Increase in global population that needs feeding.
- Increase in agricultural costs.
- Changing weather and environment.
- Impact of wars and currency changes.

Buying food for the family

We need to find ways to save money when buying and cooking food. Supermarkets advise us on how to shop and cook economically. For example, one supermarket ran a campaign to make a main course for a family of four for £5.

Using the Internet

You can compare prices of food on the Internet. The website mySupermarket compares the prices in supermarkets and helps you make the cheapest choices. It compares the cost of your food trolley in different supermarkets. You can even do the calorie count of your food and get healthier alternatives.

mySupermarket website.

WEBSITES

mySupermarket

Marguerite Patten.

How can you lower the cost of food?

- Avoid food waste – do not buy more food than you need and eat food before its 'use by' date.
- Look at special offers such as buy one get one free – but do not buy more than you need.
- Choose food that you like to eat and know how to cook – otherwise it will be wasted.
- Choose cheaper cuts of meat and types of fish.
- Use the Internet to compare prices in supermarkets and shop around.

Food writer and broadcaster Marguerite Patten was a food adviser to the government during the Second World War. She wrote: 'In the war years, food was scarce and it was a crime to waste food. Now we have a huge choice and we're not the best at doing things with leftovers.'

You pay more for better quality so, if some food is more expensive, the ingredients are probably better quality.

Cooking food

The quicker you cook food, the less it costs, so a microwave is the fastest and cheapest way to cook. Foods such as casseroles and stews need long, slow cooking. If you are using an oven, cook lots of things at the same time such as a casserole, baked potatoes and a fruit crumble to save energy costs.

INVESTIGATION

Create your own two-course meal for four people that costs under £5. Investigate the nutritional analysis for this dish and see if it is healthy.

QUESTIONS

1. Explain why the cost of food increases around the world.
2. Give three ways that a household can save money on food bills.
3. Give three ways to save money on cooking costs.

Buying goods and consumer help

A number of Acts protect you when you buy goods and services.

Acts protecting consumers	
Act	**Impact**
The Weights and Measures Act	The quantity of the contents of a pack of food must be marked on the package to show weight, volume or number.
The Sale of Goods Act 1979	Goods must be of a satisfactory quality, fit for purpose and as described.
Sale and Supply of Goods Act 1994	Goods must match the description given to them, and must be fit for purpose and of a satisfactory quality.
Sale and Supply of Goods to Consumers Regulations 2002	Buyers should have goods that are of a satisfactory quality.
Unfair Trading Regulations 2008	It is an offence for traders to treat consumers unfairly.

The Sale and Supply of Goods to Consumers Regulations 2002 Act says that buyers are entitled to goods of satisfactory quality and, if an item has a fault, the consumer can complain once it is discovered. Buyers cannot complain if the goods have had fair wear and tear, have been misused or damaged or if they decide they no longer want the item.

WEBSITES

Trading Standards Department

Citizens Advice Bureau

Office of Fair Trading

How to make a complaint

Go back to the shop as soon as possible, taking with you the goods and proof of purchase. Explain the problem and state what you want to be done. If you are not satisfied, write to the manager, if it is a large company, or think about taking the matter to court.

Consumer advice

If things go wrong and you need some advice, these are the people and organisations that can help.

Tradings Standards Officers

Trading Standards Officers investigate false or misleading descriptions, inaccurate weights or measures, unfair prices and the safety of goods. They help to protect consumers and traders against bad practice and unfair trading. Their main areas of work are:

- weights and measures – ensuring that all goods sold by weight, volume, length or area are accurately measured
- investigating misleading price claims
- ensuring that goods and services are accurately described
- price marking – shops must display the price of all goods.

You can contact your local Trading Standards Officer at your local authority.

The Consumers' Association

The Consumers' Association, also known as Which?, produces a magazine and runs an online helpline. It offers advice on different ways to make a complaint if you feel you have been unfairly treated by traders. It tells you how to deal with scams and fraud, and provides easy-to-follow guides to the laws that affect your consumer decisions.

Environmental Health Officers (EHOs)

The law makes it a criminal offence to sell consumer goods that are unsafe, or food that is unfit for you to eat or that could be harmful to your health. There are laws on how food is labelled and on the cleanliness of places where food is sold.

Environmental Health Officers are there to enforce these laws. If you buy food that is of poor quality you should contact the local Environmental Health Department. These departments can close down dirty shops and restaurants.

The Citizens Advice Bureau (CAB)

The Citizens Advice Bureau offers the public free advice on problems such as legal matters, employment, debt and consumer issues. Advisers help to negotiate with companies and can help you to complete forms and letters. There are CAB offices in most towns and there is an online service too.

The Office of Fair Trading

The Office of Fair Trading is a government department that watches out for bad trading practices and traders who might mislead or deceive consumers. You can contact it through its website.

The Consumers' Association website.

The CAB offers free advice to consumers.

Food in the news

There is always something new going on in the food world.

Nanotechnology and nanofoods

Nanotechnology is a process of manipulating materials on a very small scale. A nanometre (nm) is one-millionth of a millimetre – roughly one-80-thousandth of the width of a human hair. Nanomaterials are used in cosmetics to give them new characteristics.

Nanotechnology could be useful in food production in the areas of farming, processing and packaging. However, there is much debate on its effect on the environment and its safety.

Farming

Several 'smart' pesticides, called nanocides, have passed the tests and are licensed for use in the USA and UK. These remain harmless until they reach the stomachs of the insects they are targeting, and only then become toxic. The agrochemical companies believe that these pesticides are needed in smaller concentrations, and will be more effective and less expensive.

Packaging

Nanotechnology can be used in coatings for packaging that change colour when the food inside begins to go off. Nano labels can tell you if a fruit is ripe by changing colour.

There are currently no nanofoods in the UK. Vitamin C nanocapsules may soon be used in drinks, releasing the vitamin C when the drink is opened. Nanotechnology could be used to stabilise the nutritional properties of foods. For example, iron and omega 3 are not stable in liquids, but nanocapsules can release their nutrition when needed. This would help people with deficiencies such as anaemia.

What about safety?

Scientists are concerned that little is known about the behaviour of nanoparticles in the environment, and want the government to assess the environmental risks.

Scientist have also expressed concern about the digestion of nanoparticles, as they are small enough to travel through the gut wall and could end up anywhere in the body. They could also end up in different parts of the food chain, such as rubbish dumps and landfill.

Consumers may decide if nanofoods end up in our supermarkets. Several years ago, GM foods were launched but there was such a public outcry that GM foods were withdrawn

Vitamin C Drink

with Nanocapsule

Fruit Berry Flavour

from UK supermarkets. The EU Novel Foods Directive has strict evaluation rules for the environment and safety before anything goes on the market, including nanofoods.

Future food problems

The world's population, which is 6.5 billion today, is expected to reach nine billion by 2050. This increase will create huge pressure to provide food to feed everyone. Our demand for food will exceed our ability to produce it. Here are some issues to think about.

- Climate change will worsen the problem, as droughts prevent crops growing.
- As new economies such as China and India choose to eat a wider range of food products, the demand on global food production will increase.
- If land traditionally used for food crops is used to produce **biofuel** crops instead (like maize or sunflowers), more food will be taken away from people who will need it.

DNA food detection

As the price of food rises, scientists need methods to detect if certain 'premium' foods really are what it says on the label – for example, basmati rice or sea bream sell at a higher price than more common rice or fish, so there are profits to be made if the suppliers can escape fraud detection. Now there is a system, using DNA technology, that can identify the components of the food. This technology is also used to detect if food contains peanuts or GM materials.

New miniature sensors for analysing DNA have also been developed that can identify bacterial strains that could cause food poisoning. This will save manufacturers millions of pounds in product recalls and possible legal action, and help to keep the public safe.

Modified starch

You will see **modified starch** on many food labels. It is a product available to the food industry for use in large-scale recipes, and is used in commercial food products to thicken and stabilise sauces and desserts. It has been called a 'smart' food, as it has been altered to perform additional functions.

Starches are modified by chemical and physical means to:

- increase the stability of the food against excessive heat, acid, and freezing
- change the texture of a product
- lengthen or shorten the gelatinisation time of a product when it is made in a factory.

There are instant modified starches that thicken liquids without heat. These are used in food factories to save cooking time and to help produce products that are the same each time.

QUESTIONS

1. Give one example to show how nanotechnology could be used for foods.
2. Give two reasons why there may be a food crisis in future years.
3. What is the function of modified starch?

ExamCafé

Welcome

A place and time to study

- Work in a quiet space that is comfortable to sit in.
- Do not work every night, as you need a break.
- Eat plenty of healthy food and drink water. Avoid living off junk food and too much sugar and fat.
- If you use the Internet for revision, try not to mess about and get distracted. Keep focused on the revision task and use websites such as BBC GCSE Bitesize to help.
- Make sure you know the date, time and place of the exam and plan around this.
- Get plenty of rest – do not work through the night, as you'll be too tired to concentrate.

And good luck!

Ten tips on the day of the examination

1. On the day of the exam, when you turn the paper over, do not start writing until you have read the exam paper from cover to cover.
2. Work out where the marks are allocated and aim to write as many points as there are marks.
3. Often the most marks are awarded in the final sections, so do not leave them out.
4. Have an idea of how much time you will spend on each question, with the ones with the most marks taking the most time.
5. Answering four questions quite well is better than answering one extremely well and leaving some unfinished.
6. Make sure you answer the question on the paper and not the one you would like to answer.
7. Read through your answer before starting the next question.
8. Make sure the examiner can read your writing, try and spell and punctuate your work as well as possible.
9. Watch the clock, read through your answers before you finish.
10. Make sure you get enough rest before your next exam.

Exam question

This is a question that carries 10 marks and needs a longer answer.

a) How is the consumer protected from misleading advertising? (4 marks)
b) Explain the marketing methods that supermarkets use to increase sales of food products in their stores. (6 marks)

This is from an examiner's report to show how a candidate gets high-, mid- and low-level marks. The question is out of a total of 10 marks.

High-level response 8-10 marks
- Both parts of the question have been considered in depth. The information has sound recall and application of knowledge.
- The candidate can demonstrate accurate use of spelling, punctuation and grammar.

Mid-level response 4-7 marks
- Both parts of the question have been considered but responses may be superficial and lacking in depth. Information is reasonably well organised but may just be factual recall.
- There may be occasional errors in spelling, punctuation and grammar.
- The candidate uses some specialist terms.

Low-level response 0-3 marks
- Both aspects of the question may not have been covered.
- Information may be muddled and not used to support points made.
- There may be errors in spelling, punctuation and grammar.
- The candidate uses few, if any, specialist terms.

Some key points in the answers
Section a) is worth 4 marks; section b) is worth 6 marks.

Section a)
- People can complain to the local authority Trading Standards Department, who will investigate.
- The Advertising Standards Authority (ASA) is an independent body that regulates the advertising industry. The ASA code of practice says an advert must be 'legal, decent, honest and truthful'.
- Ofcom (Office of Communications) is an independent organisation that regulates the UK's broadcasting, telecommunications and wireless communications sectors.
- People can complain directly to the organisation that made the advert.

Section b)
- Product placement helps to increase sales and make people aware of products.
- Special offers include money off, buy one get one free, 30 per cent extra in a product, gifts with the product and competitions to enter. These all encourage people to buy.
- Loyalty cards give shoppers money off and vouchers.
- Supermarkets sell a food at a price less than cost price to encourage customers to buy more food. This is called a loss leader.
- Eye level is buy level – this is the most popular shelf position for people to buy from.
- The shop may have special facilities, such as a coffee shop.
- You may find promotions and offers on the sales receipt.

Making food to eat, cooking skills

During your assessment, you will make food for people to eat. The way food looks, tastes and smells is very important. Before you eat, you look at the food and decide whether you want to eat it.

Food checks to think about when planning and serving food

Appearance

You might judge the appearance of food to see if it looks fresh, healthy or appetising. The presentation of the food is important. Food should be served on clean, attractive dishes that complement it.

Colour

We expect food to be a certain colour. We might reject a raw apple that has gone brown, or green custard, because these are not colours that we would expect. Food manufacturers add colours to food products to make them more attractive. You can make meals look colourful and attractive with garnishes such as parsley, herbs and colourful vegetables.

Texture

We judge food by its texture. Try to get a range of textures in a meal. Rice with fish in white sauce may need the addition of food with a crunchy texture such as a tossed salad.

Smell

Smell matters. If something smells burnt, we do not eat it. Our sense of smell is useful in judging the safety of food: we smell off flavours and reject the food. Smell is part of food's attraction – the smell of baking bread is very tempting.

Taste and flavour

Taste is detected by the taste buds in the mouth. Different areas of the tongue detect the four basic tastes: sweet, sour, bitter and salt. Flavour is a combination of taste and smell. If you have a cold, you cannot taste properly.

How does it sound?

We do judge food on its sound. Think of the crunch of an apple or piece of celery, the 'snap' of a crisp biscuit or crisps, and even the 'snap, crackle and pop' of some breakfast cereals.

Temperature matters

Serve food at the right temperature. Hot food should be served hot, and not left to keep warm and become dried up and tired. Cold food should be chilled until ready to serve.

TO DO

Create a two-course meal and show which of the food checks you have included.

For example, mashed potato is decorated with parsley – adding colour.

What are cooking skills?

In the controlled assessment, you must show cooking skills and awareness of health and safety. Examples of cooking skills, are shown in blue and health and safety shown in red.

Getting ready to cook

- Preparing yourself to cook by washing hands and putting on an apron or overall.
- Storing food safely and organising your work surface efficiently.
- Working hygienically – not licking food.
- Covering food and putting it away when it is not used.

Using tools and equipment

- Chopping, peeling with a knife – knowing how to cut things efficiently and safely.
- Measuring things accurately, such as weighing ingredients for a recipe.
- Grating things safely such as cheese.
- Using the right spoon for the task – not stirring a saucepan with a metal spoon.
- Knowing how to handle meat and chicken safely.
- Keeping chilled food cold and not leaving vegetables to soak in water.
- Using food processors and mixers to show skilful handling of this equipment to get the right consistency for a dish and using the machinery safely.
- Preparing pastry and rolling it out – getting the consistency right.
- Shaping things and making flans that have an even amount of pastry.
- Making bread dough and baking it successfully.
- Shaping burgers, fish cakes and veggie burgers then cooking them well.

Cooking

- Using an oven safely and knowing which temperature and shelves to use.
- For example, baking things so that they are well cooked and not raw.
- Using the hob safely – not overcooking food or preparing things dangerously.
- Boiling things with lids on for the right amount of time – for example, rice.
- Using the microwave safely and for the correct time.
- Knowing when something is done and ready to eat.
- Making sauces that are the right consistency.
- Frying things such as onions and stir-fried vegetables so they are just cooked.
- Preparing potatoes – mashing them smoothly.
- Serving hot food hot and cold food cold.
- Presenting things so that they look attractive – cleaning the dishes and garnishing food.
- Clearing away rubbish and washing up well.
- Not wasting food.

TO DO

Make a list of ten food skills that you could show when preparing and cooking food.

Make a list of ten health and safety issues that you need to consider when making food.

Tasting and testing 1

Sensory analysis

Tasting food is known as sensory analysis, and is used to make judgements about the quality of food and how it tastes. You will need to carry out a sensory analysis for all the food that you make for assessments.

Sensory analysis is used to analyse and interpret reactions to the characteristics of food by the senses of sight, smell, taste and hearing. These characteristics are the organoleptic properties of food.

Everyone's taste is different, so when food is tasted professionally, the tasting panel must agree on the words used to describe food.

Why do companies need to taste food?

Manufacturers use tasting panels to find out if people like or dislike new products they develop. As people have different tastes, food companies need to carry out a range of tasting tests to discover what people like. From the results, they know how to change the product and alter the ingredients to appeal to more people. They must carry out tests again to make sure they have made the right changes.

Tasting in the classroom

It is important to get other people's views if you are making food for a specific target group. If you are designing a food for a young child, student or older person, you need to test your product and dishes on people from your target group.

Setting up a tasting panel

For a tasting panel, you can use a few people or get the views of many people. You must instruct them clearly and design a tasting chart for them to complete.

Setting up a tasting area

During a tasting session, the tasters should understand that no one has the right answer. Tasters should not talk and share ideas or look at the expressions of others.

Tips for tasting food

- Set up a special, quiet tasting area that is well lit.
- Put food in identical, plain containers and serve all samples in the same way and at the same temperature.

TO DO

1. Create your own 'word bank' of sensory descriptors that can be used to describe food products.

2. Describe the appearance, taste, mouthfeel and smell of the following foods:
   a) an apple
   b) hot bread
   c) a fizzy fruit drink.
   Add examples of your own. You could use a table like the one shown below.

Appearance and colour	Taste and flavour
Mouthfeel/texture, consistency	**Smell or odour**

- Allow the taster to sip water or eat a plain biscuit between each tasting to clear the palate.
- Do not give them too much to taste, otherwise their taste buds will get tired.
- Code the samples of food randomly to avoid the tasters having a preference.
- Make sure they understand how to taste the food and fill in any charts.

Sensory descriptors

When we taste food, we are judging several factors:

- appearance and colour
- taste and flavour
- mouthfeel/texture, consistency
- smell or odour.

The words used as descriptions are known as sensory descriptors.

Examples of sensory descriptors

Appearance and colour: attractive, healthy, greasy, creamy, golden, orange, bright, dull

Taste and flavour: fruity, sweet, bitter, sour, salty, sharp, spicy, tangy

Mouthfeel/texture, consistency: hard, soft, rubbery, crispy, lumpy, dry, smooth

Smell or odour: fragrant, burnt, herby, garlicky, fishy.

QUESTIONS

1. Give two reasons why food companies run tasting panels to test their food products.
2. List three points to consider when setting up a tasting panel.
3. Give an example of three sensory descriptors that could be used for apples.

Tasting and testing 2

Fair testing

Fair testing is important when tasting and comparing similar food products. Make sure that you are comparing like with like. Food should be served in similar-sized portions, on similar plates or cups, and at the same temperature.

Different tests are used in sensory analysis to obtain different kinds of information.

Paired comparison test

Tasters are asked to say which of two samples they prefer, or which is sweeter or spicier.

Triangle tests

Triangle tests are used to see if people can tell the difference between food products. For example, can you tell the difference between one brand of crisp and another? These tests are used by food companies when they want to develop a 'me too' product – one that may be similar to another on the market.

Ranking test

This test sorts foods into an order. For example, the taster could be asked to place five yogurts in the order he or she likes them best. The taster could also rank the yogurts in order of sweetness. Ranking can be used by manufacturers to find the most popular flavour of crisps by sorting between eight and ten flavours in order. They then decide which one to produce.

> **FACT**
>
> A survey of 9,000 Danish schoolchildren found that girls have a better sense of taste than boys. This research could help in producing healthier snacks. The survey showed that boys need 10 per cent more sourness and 20 per cent more sweetness to recognise a taste. So foods for boys might need extreme and sour flavours.

Ranking Tasting Chart to find information

Tick a box for each section ☐

Overall opinion on food
☐ like very much ☐ like moderately ☐ neither like nor dislike ☐ dislike ☐ dislike a lot

Appearance
☐ like very much ☐ like moderately ☐ neither like nor dislike ☐ dislike ☐ dislike a lot

Taste
☐ like very much ☐ like moderately ☐ neither like nor dislike ☐ dislike ☐ dislike a lot

Smell

☐ like very much ☐ like moderately ☐ neither like nor dislike ☐ dislike ☐ dislike a lot

Texture
☐ like very much ☐ like moderately ☐ neither like nor dislike ☐ dislike ☐ dislike a lot

---

This type of chart is very useful as it tells you if people like the food and, if there is a low score for any of the sections you know where to make changes.

Rating chart

Rating tests give you scores for tasting. This chart uses stars. Three stars means excellent, two stars means good, one star means OK.

	Appearance	Taste	Smell	Texture
Vegetable bake	**	***	*	*

To evaluate this vegetable bake, the chart shows that the texture and smell need changing to make it better.

Rating test

Star profile, star diagram or radar chart

A star profile can show the sensory descriptors for the food. People on the tasting panel can rate each sensory descriptor to give the product a tasting profile. The results can be compared to see what people think about the product.

For the star profile, use a scale of 0–5, and rate each descriptor where 0 = not and 5 = very, as you see in the example.

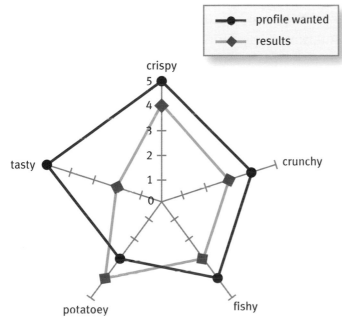

A star profile for fish cakes.

TO DO

1. Draw a star profile for each of the following foods to show the sensory descriptors you would use in a tasting session:

   a) tomato and cheese pizza

   b) fruit yogurt

   c) salt and vinegar crisps

   d) apple pie.

Assessment

Controlled assessment

Home Economics has a 60 per cent weighting for controlled assessments which may have up to three separate tasks, each with a minimum 20 per cent weighting. The GCSE Boards provide guidance on word or time limits and may or may not suggest the tasks, so you need to check when you start.

Areas to be covered in the controlled assessment

- Evaluate research.
- Gather research information from primary and secondary sources.
- Present information using suitable techniques.
- Carry out practical work.
- Evaluate practical work.
- Carry out sensory and nutritional analysis linked to task analysis.
- Interpret evidence with reference to the issues identified in task analysis.
- Justify any changes you make. Identify strengths and areas for improvement.
- Produce a report on the conclusions drawn from the investigations – consider if you have achieved aims and if the action was appropriate.

Getting started with controlled assessments

- Be aware of the criteria for assessment.
- Know the time for the task or the number of words that can be used.
- Be clear about the meaning of the task given to you or chosen for you.
- You can use computer software and the Internet for presenting work.

Investigational work
- Identify issues and questions within the context of the task.
- Use a range of primary and secondary sources relevant to the topic.
- Sources of information should be quoted.
- *Avoid copying from any source.*

Selection and development of ideas
- For the task, create a clear plan of action and aims.
- Throughout the task, draw conclusions with justification.
- Select and organise and explore a number of ideas.
- Include detailed and useful annotation of work.

Planning and making
- Apply knowledge and understanding to plan and take action with analysis and adaptations as necessary.
- Show awareness of health and safety skills.

- Show evidence of application of knowledge and practical skills in making.
- Use appropriate presentation of techniques for the finished result(s).
- Show understanding of the requirements of the task.

Evaluation
- You need detailed sensory testing.
- Evaluate the effectiveness and appropriateness of planning.
- Arrive at a personal point of view.
- Use evidence to support conclusions and show understanding of the requirements of the task.
- Show an appreciation of the strengths and weaknesses of the task and the identification of possible further developments.

Task analysis

First look closely the task. Here are some examples.

Task 1
Many young students live away from home and eat takeaway food and ready meals. Investigate what foods they like and make a range of nutritious dishes that would be economical and easy to make, and would meet their dietary requirements.

Task 2
Investigate one special dietary need and prepare a selection of interesting dishes that would be suitable for a person who has the dietary need studied.

Task 3
Investigate ways in which the dietary needs of an elderly person living alone can be met. Plan and prepare a range of nutritious dishes that a healthy, active, 75-year-old person could make.

Task 4
Calcium is an important nutrient for developing strong bones and teeth. Plan and make two food items that are high in calcium. Use nutritional data to support the choice of items to make.

Analyse the task

Highlight the key words. In Task 4 these are:

1. **Plan and make**
2. **two food items**
3. **high in calcium**
4. **Use nutritional data to support choice.**

Think of using a mind map or spider diagram or just bullet points, as below.

- I need to find foods that are high in calcium.
- I need a way to get the nutritional information for the items.
- I need to know what 'high in calcium' means.
- I need to make two dishes that are attractive and nutritious.

Research

For research, you are asked to carry out primary and secondary research.

Primary research

This is finding out your own information direct from the source. There are different ways to collect original information for primary research, including:

- **questionnaires** – to find out people's views and how popular things are.
- **surveys** – to find information on what is happening.
- **emails or letters** – to find out what products are available in a range.
- **interviews** – to ask people what foods they like best.
- **product analysis** – by using existing products.
- **observations** – looking at how people choose food for school lunch.
- **costings** – if the task asks for the cost of a dish or meal.
- **case studies** – of how people eat.
- **shop visits**, for example, to see a range of vegetarian products.

This original information is essential for your work.

Secondary research

This is getting information from existing sources. Sources include:

- Internet research
- textbooks, newspapers and magazines
- radio and TV programmes
- databases with sources of information.

Do not copy the work directly from these sources. Keep a record of each source to use in your work.

Questionnaires

You need a viable sample of people to ask and the questions should be relevant to the people in the sample. Check with the exam board how many people make a viable sample. For example, for Task 1 (page 185), you need to ask some students and may only be able to find up to ten for your sample. You need to include evaluation of results of questionnaires and justification for the practical work.

Designing a questionnaire

Before you write the questions, jot down what you need to find out. What is the point of the questionnaire? What useful information are you trying to find out? For example, in Task 1 you need to ask some students what foods they do and do not like to eat, as this will help when planning some meals.

After you have written the questions, use ICT to help with the questionnaire.

Use a word processing package such as Word® to write the questionnaire.

Use a database program such as Excel® to record your answers and analyse them.

Here are some examples of surveys you could carry out that would need questionnaires.

1. How often do people eat out and how much do they spend?
2. What is the cost of a family meal for four?
3. What special safety issues are needed when designing food that elderly people can cook?

Evaluating your research

For each piece of research, write brief notes on:

- what you did
- the aims of the research – what you wanted to find out
- what you found out
- how you will use your findings to choose dishes
- any extra comments – for example, 'I should have asked more people'.

This research then gives you a clear course of action, as the following example shows.

TO DO

Make a copy of the table below. Look at the selection of tasks on page 185 and show what type of research you would carry out for each one and what the aim of the research would be. One example has been completed.

	Type of research	Aim
Task 1	Use a questionnaire to find out what food students like. Look at student cookbooks and get ideas for recipes.	To find the foods they like and dislike with reasons. To get ideas for recipes.
Task 2		
Task 3		
Task 4		

My research has shown that for my elderly person I need to make dishes that are easy to handle, don't involve frying in fat or lifting heavy things out of the oven. This information came from my interviews with elderly people, who said they had trouble lifting heavy tins out of the oven.

State the aims linked to the research analysis

For example, the dishes for the student in Task 1 must meet the criteria of being nutritious, economical, easy to make and meeting their dietary requirements. You need to explain these criteria a bit more clearly:

- 'nutritious' means they have a balance of nutrients
- 'economical' means they cost under £2 a portion
- 'easy to make' will mean that the skills are simple and cooking time quick
- 'meets their dietary requirements' means that they provide the correct nutrients for that age group.

This table shows a range of dishes and the criteria to see if they have been met.

	Nutritious	Economical	Easy to make	Meets their dietary requirements
Baked potato with chilli sauce	Yes	Yes	Yes	Yes
Lasagne with salad	Yes	Yes	Yes	Yes
Pasta bake	Yes	Yes	Yes	Yes
Apple crumble	Yes	Yes	Yes	Yes
Sweet and sour chicken with rice	Yes	Yes	Yes	Yes
Pizza with mushrooms	Yes	Yes	Yes	Yes
Shepherd's pie	Yes	Yes	Yes	Yes
Risotto	Yes	Yes	Yes	Yes

All these dishes meet the criteria of the task. Some need more skill to make than others and are more interesting. In our example, the cost needs to be tested to make sure dishes are under £2 a portion.

Make a final choice, depending on the exam board requirements.

Planning a practical solution to the task

Make a plan of action. This could be a timeplan, flow chart, log or diary. Planning should include methods and ingredients, details of recipes, sensory testing and investigations.

- A timeplan can be set in a table and give times for events to happen.
- A flow diagram shows the flow of the progress.
- A log or a diary is a step-by-step progress of the work.

Planning using a timeplan

The task could be to find out how cultural influences are changing the range of ready-made meals available in supermarkets. These are the steps in the planning.

- Carry out a shopping survey using the Internet and a shop visit to find out what is for sale.
- Take the food of one culture, such as Caribbean food or Indian food, and make a typical dish.
- Compare this dish with the cost and nutritional value of the ready-made version.
- Carry out a comparative tasting to compare results.
- Evaluate the investigation. Produce a written report on the outcomes.

Plan	Time for each section
Carry out research using the Internet.	1 hour
Carry out shopping survey of one culture.	$1\frac{1}{2}$ hours
Select one or two dishes, and plan and make them and compare tastes and costs.	3 hours
Evaluate investigation and make report.	1–2 hours

Detailed planning

Each section of the timeplan needs to be broken down into more detail, to include information about health and safety and the cooking skills that you will be using. The timeplan opposite shows the time needed to make the dish, and the health and safety and skills for a vegetable bean bake.

Time	Method	Health and safety	Skills
	Timeplan for vegetable bean bake		
9	Collect all the ingredients and equipment.		
9.05	Chop onion, garlic, tomatoes, peppers and carrot.	Handle knife with care.	Chopping skills
9.20	Fry onion and garlic.	Take care with hot pan.	Frying skills
9.27	Add carrot and tomatoes, tomato purée and stir fry.	Do not splash ingredients.	Handling of cooking
9.30	Add peppers and cover and simmer.	Do not burn pan.	Temperature management
9.35	Add can of beans, and season with salt and pepper.		Cooking skills
9.40	Spoon into dish and sprinkle on grated cheese. Bake 10 mins.	Handle hot dishes carefully.	Keeping dishes clean, baking
9.50	Remove and garnish ready for tasting.	Put on wooden board to protect from heat.	Attractive presentation
10.00	Carry out tasting.	Do this hygienically.	Fair tasting

Tasting and testing

You may want to compare your dish with a ready-made meal. If so, make sure both dishes are served at the same temperature and do not identify the home-made and bought ones. You could choose from a variety of tests.

- **Rating tests** – the tasters give the product a score out of 5 on how much they like it, where 1 = not much and 5 = like a lot.
- **Smiley face chart** – this chart shows very quickly if people like, dislike or do not know if they like your dish.
- **The star profile** is useful as it compares one dish with another.

Evaluating results

Tasting results

Record the results of your tasting:

'Most people liked the home-made vegetable bean bake best because it was colourful and tasty.'

You can evaluate on the star profile result.

Costing results

You can compare the costs of 100 grams of ready-made food with 100 grams of your homemade dish – but make sure the ingredients are really similar, otherwise it is not a fair test.

Present evaluations and conclusions

You need to evaluate and test at each stage. This information includes the research, evaluation, practical and results of tasting.

- Identify strengths and areas for improvement.
- Produce a report on the conclusions drawn from the investigations.
- Consider if you have achieved your aims and if action was appropriate.

Task analysis

This is an example of a task that has been researched, planned, made and evaluated.

Task

Children need to have healthier choices for their food and drink.

- Investigate the need for healthier choices.
- Develop a range of interesting ideas that could form part of children's meals.
- Make a plan to show how you will make a selection of children's meal dishes.
- Make and present a selection of dishes.
- Evaluate your work.

Work to support the task

- I need evidence of interpretation, research and investigation, using ICT.
- I need to show the development of ideas with reasons for rejection and selection.
- I need to set clear aims for the investigation.
- I must identify issues and questions.
- I must select and develop ideas.
- I must make a plan of action.
- I must explore a number of ideas and make a reasoned choice.
- I must analyse and adapt if needed.

Practical outcome

- I must show evidence of knowledge and skills in outcome.
- I must show awareness of health and safety.

Evaluation

- I will evaluate planning methods and results used.
- I will show strengths and weaknesses of task with suggestions for development.

Aims of investigation

The aim is to find out if children need to have healthier choices of meals, and what foods they would like to eat if they had a choice. Then develop meals that might appeal to them. I need to find out:

- food choices that might be made for children's meals and how to make them healthier
- types of drinks that are served at the moment
- what is a healthy choice? Look at traffic light system for products.

Types of research to be used

- Questionnaire and interviews to find out what children eat – I need to decide on age group, so will visit local primary school.
- I will choose evening meal as the focus.
- Analyse the results to find out if they are healthy or not using a nutritional analysis program.
- Find out what healthy eating means – use textbooks and the Internet.
- Make decisions after research to develop some easy to prepare healthy meals.

Plan of action

- I will find what foods are popular for meals, based on results of questionnaire and interviews.
- I will find similar but healthier recipes for foods and drinks to make and test.
- I will produce a detailed plan of action and follow it through.
- After tasting, I will find out which ones are the best.

Carrying out the plan

- I will prepare a series of dishes and taste, nutritionally analyse and cost the dishes.

Evaluation

- I will comment on choices and I will make suggestions for further development.

Ideas for research

- Product analysis – look at things that are available.
- Use the Internet – supermarket sites. Sainsbury's website shows a range of products for children.

Note: The number of dishes you make depends on the exam board.

List of ideas		
	Comments	**Final choice**
Vegetable pasta bake	Children like this	Yes
Baked potato with fillings		
Chilli con carne with rice		
Sweet and sour chicken with rice		Yes
Lasagne		
Cottage pie		
Macaroni cheese with broccoli		Yes
Chicken nuggets with mashed potato		
Desserts		
Fruit crumble		Yes
Trifle with fresh fruit		
Fruit salad with crunchy topping		

Complete a timeplan or order of work.

Time plan		
Order of work	**Special points**	**Health and safety**

Complete this for each dish.

- Evaluation – I will use a simple rating chart for each dish.
- Get the opinion of five to ten people.
- Each person can score with up to five stars for appearance, texture and taste.

Dish	Appearance	Texture	Taste
Vegetable pasta bake	***	***	****
Macaroni cheese with broccoli	****	***	**

Final evaluation will include comments on the work done in research, investigations, planning, making and tasting. Then I will write about any changes that could be made and comment on the choices that I have made.

ICT for food work

A computer can be used in many ways to improve and speed up food work.

Programs that can be used

Type of program	How can it be used?
Word processing	Writing letters, creating questionnaires, writing up coursework. Completing a timeplan for the practical work. You can draw a flow chart in Word® for planning.
Using a: a) nutritional database b) recipe database	Nutritional database – used to analyse recipes and modify them to make them healthier, working out daily diet, menu creation. Recipe database – storing recipes and identifying ingredients.
Spreadsheets	Spreadsheets are used for calculations such as the cost of a recipe, how to increase the size of a recipe to serve larger numbers of people and costing a product for sale. Spreadsheets such as Excel® are valuable for tasting work to create and display results, especially drawing star profiles.
Graphics from spreadsheets	You can quickly display the information on a spreadsheet in the form of graphs, pie charts, and radar charts. This improves the presentation and accuracy of your work.
Desktop publishing	Coursework can be presented very smartly using a desktop publishing package. Text and pictures can be created on the screen and page layout designed.
Using the Internet	There is a vast amount of information available on the Internet. Try to use recognised sites for the research, although a Google search will find the top sites for the information that you need.
Using a digital camera	Use the pictures to keep a record of work as you progress through the task. Keep a final picture of the dish or dishes that you have made. Use the images for evaluation and comments.
Using Excel® to produce star profiles	This is a very useful tool for tasting and evaluating food products.
Timetabling	This can be done in Excel® or Word®.

Using the Internet

- You can use search engines such as Google to get information.
- Supermarket sites are packed with information that can be used for research.
- Organisations such as the British Nutrition Foundation, the Food Standards Agency and the Vegetarian Society all provide valuable information for research.
- BBC GCSE Bitesize is a good site for revision.

Keep a record of the sites that you use.

Electronically controlled assessment

Electronic controlled assessment is designed to give candidates an opportunity to demonstrate what they can do using current technology. Evidence can be submitted in word-processed documents, PowerPoint® presentations, digital photo and digital video. Word® and PowerPoint® presentations may need to be converted into a format agreed by the examining board.

So there will be many exciting ways of presenting assessments and you will be able to make presentations, podcasts and videos of your work.

Food Acts

This section contains a brief overview of some of the most important laws relating to food in the UK.

Consumer Protection from Unfair Trading Regulations 2008

The Regulations introduce new rules about consumer protection and the responsibility of businesses to trade fairly. It is an offence for traders to treat consumers unfairly.

Food Hygiene (England) Regulations 2006

This requires all food businesses to put in place procedures which are based on the principles of Hazard Analysis and Critical Control Points (HACCP). There is a legal requirement on all food businesses to provide appropriate documents and records showing how the HACCP principles are being applied. Most food businesses will need to register all of their premises, and follow strict hygiene regulations.

Food Labelling Regulations 1996

The principal provisions of the regulations are to require all food which is ready for delivery to the ultimate consumer or to a catering establishment, subject to certain exceptions, to be marked or labelled with:

- the name of the food
- a list of ingredients
- the appropriate durability indication
- any special storage conditions or conditions of use
- the name and address of the manufacturer or packer or of a seller and in certain cases:
- particulars of the place of origin of the food
- instructions for use.

Food Safety (General Food Hygiene) Regulations 1995

These regulations cover general requirements for the design, construction and operation of food premises. The premises must be designed to allow food to be prepared safely with minimal risk of cross-contamination. The design must allow for adequate cleaning and/or disinfection. The kitchen should be at least one-third of the size of the dining area and planned so that work flows progressively from delivery of goods to service of the food. "Dirty" work, such as washing/preparing raw food and washing up, should be carried out away from preparation of ready-to-eat foods.

Food Safety (Temperature Control) Regulations 1995

Food which is susceptible to the bacteria, toxins and viruses that can cause food poisoning needs to be stored at the correct temperature. The Regulations require potentially dangerous foods to be held at or below 8°C or above 63°C. Certain exceptions are allowed for practical considerations relating to, for example, processing or handling food, as long as food safety is not put at risk. The regulations do not list specific foods which need to be held under temperature control conditions and food businesses should decide for themselves which foods should be held under temperature control.

Food Safety Act 1990

The Food Safety Act 1990 regulates the statutory obligation to treat food intended for human consumption in a controlled and managed way. The key requirements of the Act are that food must comply with food safety requirements, must be "of the nature, substance and quality demanded", and must be correctly described (labelled).

Food Standards Act 1999

This Act sets out the Food Standards Agency's main objective of protecting public health in relation to food and the functions that it will assume in pursuit of that aim, and gives the Agency the powers necessary to enable it to act in the consumer's interest at any stage in the food production and supply chain. The Act provides for the Agency's main organisational and accountability arrangements. In addition, it provides powers to establish a scheme for the notification of the results of tests for food-borne diseases.

General Food Law Regulation 2002

EC legislation on general food safety.

General Food Law Regulation 2004

Provides amendments for the regulations 2002 and amends the Food Safety Act 1990.

Hazard Analysis and Critical Control Points (HACCP)

HACCP is a systematic preventive approach to food safety and pharmaceutical safety that addresses physical, chemical, and biological hazards as a means of prevention rather than finished product inspection. HACCP is used in the food industry to identify potential food safety hazards, so that key actions, known as Critical Control Points (CCPs) can be taken to reduce or eliminate the risk of the hazards being realised. The system is used at all stages of food production and preparation processes including packaging, distribution, etc.

Licensing laws

The Licensing Act 2003 introduced new types of licence and changes the way alcohol licensing is controlled. The new licensing Act intended to increase the prevention of crime and disorder, public safety, the prevention of public nuisance, and the protection of children from harm. One major change was the new personal licence. Before alcohol can be supplied the person selling or supplying the alcohol must have a personal licence or be authorised to supply the alcohol by someone who holds a personal licence.

Sale and Supply of Goods Act 1994

Goods should:
- match the description given to them
- be of a satisfactory quality
- be fit for purpose.

Sale and Supply of Goods to Consumers Regulations 2002

Buyers are entitled to goods of satisfactory quality and if an item has a fault the consumer can complain once it is discovered.

Sale of Goods Act 1979

The Sale of Goods Act 1979 regulates contracts in which goods are sold and bought. Goods must be of a satisfactory quality, fit for purpose and as described. Within six months, beginning at the time at which the goods were delivered, the buyer can require the seller to repair the goods, reduce the price, or rescind (revesting property and requiring the return of any payment) the contract where the buyer successfully claims that the goods were not in accordance with the contract at the time of delivery.

Supply of Goods and Services Act 1982

This requires a supplier of a service to carry out that service with reasonable care and skill and, unless agreed to the contrary, within a reasonable time and make no more than a reasonable charge. If a supplier of a service breaches the conditions of a contract (for example, by failing to carry out the work ordered) the consumer can either claim compensation from the trader or cancel the contract. Often reasonable compensation in these circumstances will be repair or replacement.

Trade Descriptions Act 1968

This prevents manufacturers, retailers or service industry providers from misleading consumers. Each product sold must be:
- as described: refers to any advert or verbal description made by the trader
- satisfactory quality: covers minor and cosmetic defects as well as substantial problems, and means that products must last a reasonable time. But it doesn't give you any rights if a fault was obvious or pointed out to you at point of sale
- fit for purpose: covers not only the obvious purpose of an item but any purpose you queried and were given assurances about by the trader.

Weights and Measures Act

The quantity of the contents of a pack of food must be marked on the package to show weight, volume or number. For example, if a bottle of milk is for sale and has a label saying it contains one litre, then the law states that it must contain that amount.

Glossary

5 A DAY campaign a government campaign encouraging us to eat five portions of fruit and vegetables a day

Accelerated Freeze Drying (AFD) where food is frozen and dried under vacuum

Advertising informing people about products, services or events, and persuading people to buy things

Ambient temperature room temperature

Anaphylactic shock a potentially fatal condition caused by allergy to certain foods

Anorexia nervosa an eating disorder where people restrict the amount of food they eat

Antioxidants chemicals found in vitamins A, C and E that help protect the body from disease

AOAC fibre fibre as defined by the American Association of Analytical Chemists, including a lignin and resistant starch

Bacteria single-celled organisms that are useful, but can be harmful

Basal metabolic rate (BMR) the energy used when the body is at rest

'Best before' date code used on foods with short to medium shelf life

Binge drinking when people drink excessive amounts of alcohol in a short time

Biodegradable packaging packaging that can be broken down by other living organisms

Biodigester a machine that changes food waste into electricity and biofertiliser

Biofuels fuels made from food crops

Bioyogurt yogurt with added bacteria to aid digestion

Body Mass Index (BMI) a method for estimating body fat

Browning when starch is heated to a high temperature

Bulking agents ingredients that are cheap and add volume to food products

Coeliac disease gluten intolerance – foods with gluten cannot be eaten

Combination or **composite foods** foods that contain foods from several groups on the eatwell plate

Complex carbohydrates polysaccharides that are made up of glucose units, including starch

Conduction when heat is conducted from molecule to molecule in solids or liquids

Consumers people who use things

Convection when heat travels round liquids and air by convection currents

Convenience food food that is ready-prepared to make it easy to cook and eat

Cook-chill food food that is cooked then chilled to very low temperatures

Coronary heart disease a disease linked to high fat intake

Cross-contamination when bacteria cross from one food to another

Cryogenic freezing or **immersion freezing** when food is immersed or sprayed with liquid nitrogen

Danger zone the temperature range 5–63 °C, when food can be spoiled and become dangerous to eat

Deficiency of a mineral when the mineral is in poor supply in the diet

Dehydration when the body is short of water

Dental caries tooth decay

Dietary reference values (DRVs) a series of estimates of the amount of energy and nutrients needed by different groups of healthy people in the UK population.

Estimated Average Requirements (EARs) Estimated Average Requirements for energy

eatwell plate a 'plate' diagram showing the proportions of the different food groups that we should eat to maintain a healthy and well-balanced diet

Emulsify help fat and oil disperse in very fine droplets

Energy balance when energy in from food is the same as energy out from activities – it is the right amount of energy for our body needs

Englyst method a method of fibre analysis used for NSP measurement

E-number a number showing that the additive has been accepted as safe by the countries of the European Union

Enzymes proteins that speeds up a chemical reaction but is not used up in the process

Essential amino acids amino acids that have to be eaten, as the body cannot make them

Ethical to do with morals, whether something is right or wrong

Expenditure and Food Survey the government survey that finds out what foods we are eating and trends in our eating habits

Fairtrade trade that aims to give producers a fair price for what they grow or make, and to help them improve their working conditions

Farmers' market a local market that sells locally produced food

Food allergy a type of intolerance that involves the immune system

Food fortification adding nutrients to food products

Food intolerance when the body reacts to a certain food or food ingredient

Food miles the distance food travels from source to plate

Food probe a cookery instrument used to measure the temperature inside food

Food Standards Agency a UK government body that deals with food issues

Freedom Food and **Red Tractor** marks that show animals are reared with care

Functional foods foods that claim to have health-promoting properties

Gadgets pieces of equipment that may or may not be useful in food preparation

Gelatinisation when starch breaks down when heated with water to thicken mixtures

Genetically Modified food food grown from or using plants that have been genetically changed in some way

Gluten the protein formed when wheat flour is mixed with liquid

Glycaemic index the measure of the effects of carbohydrates on blood glucose levels

Glycogen the form in which carbohydrate is stored in the liver

Halal food that is prepared according to Islamic principles

Healthy balanced diet a diet containing a variety of types of food in the right proportions to promote good health

Hidden fat fat that you cannot see in a food product

High-risk foods foods that can only be stored for a short time before they become unsafe to eat

Homogenisation breaking down the fat globules in milk

Irradiated food food bombarded with ionising rays

Kilojoules/kilocalories measures of the energy value of a food product

Kosher food that meets Jewish dietary laws and must follow special rules

Labour-saving machinery machinery designed to save time and effort

Lactation producing milk after pregnancy

Lacto ovo vegetarians vegetarians who do not eat meat, but eat eggs and dairy products

Lacto vegetarians vegetarians who do not eat meat or eggs, but eat dairy products

Legume an upright or climbing bean or pea plant

Listeria and **salmonella** food poisoning bacteria

Lower Reference Nutrient Intake (LRNI) for people with lower nutrient needs

Macronutrients foods such as protein, fat and carbohydrate, which are needed in larger amounts

Marketing the process of finding out if there is a demand for a product and ways to sell it

Metabolism a set of reactions needed to keep the body functioning

Micronutrients vitamins and minerals that are needed in smaller amounts

Microwaves waves that vibrate the fat and water molecules producing heat

Mobius loop a loop with a single twist in it, used as recycling symbol

Modified atmosphere packaging (MAP) packaging where the oxygen in packs is replaced to prolong shelf life

Modified starch non-food starch that has been changed so that it can be used by the food industry in processing

Monosaccharide the simplest form of carbohydrate molecules

Moulds a form of fungi

Nanotechnology the process of manipulating materials on a microscale

Neural tube defects problems in unborn babies that can lead to spina bifida

Non-milk extrinsic sugars (NMES) sugars found in table sugar, sweets, sugary drinks and cakes

Non-starch polysaccharide (NSP) contains insoluble and soluble fibre

Novel foods foods invented for us to eat, rather than grown or farmed naturally

Nutritional standards standards that set limits for nutritional goals

Nutritionally dense foods foods that are a good source of several nutrients

Obese when someone is obese, it means they have put on so much weight, it is dangerous for their health

Ofcom, ASA the bodies that oversee the codes of practice for the advertising industry

Omega 3 fatty acids fatty acids found in oily fish that are important for a healthy heart

Osteoporosis a disease where the bones become fragile and can break

Pasteurised milk milk that has been heated to kill harmful micro-organisms

Pathogenic bacteria those that cause illness

Pester power a term used by advertisers and marketing teams referring to children's ability to nag their parents into buying things they may not otherwise buy

pH scale the scale for measuring acids and alkalis

Polylactic acid a chemical used for biodegradable packaging

Portions the sizes and weights of food we eat

Preservation stopping food going bad

Pulses include beans and lentils, and are the seeds of plants called legumes

Quorn a mycoprotein that comes in many shapes and sizes.

Radiation when heat travels in waves or rays

Raising agents added to make mixtures rise

Reference Nutrient Intakes (RNIs) an estimate of the amount that should meet the needs of most people

Saturated fats fats that come from animal sources and can be bad for our health; they are linked to heart disease

Shelf life the length of time a food will keep

Shopping online placing an order on the Internet

Shortening fats used to make baked products crumbly

Soya protein protein from soya beans made into TVP and soya mince

Staple foods foods that make up the main part of a traditional diet, and are usually starch

Star ratings the symbols found on frozen food compartments

Starch a polysaccharide, and a carbohydrate

Sugar a preservative, sweetener and bulking agent, and a carbohydrate

Supplements extra nutrients that can be eaten for health reasons

Sustainable being able to keep something going for some time

Traffic light system shows how healthy a product is

Trans fats similar to saturated fats in their effect on health

Unsaturated fats fats thought to be beneficial to our health

'Use by' date code used on foods with a short shelf life

Vegans vegetarians who do not eat any food from animals

Weaning when babies change over from milk to solid food

Yeast a micro-organism that changes food; fungi that ferment

Index

A

accelerated freeze drying (AFD) 148
acids in cooking 126–7
additives 104–5
adults 66–7
advertising 160–1
Advertising Standards Authority (ASA) 160–1
aeration 114, 121, 122
age and diet
  adults 66–7
  babies 58–9
  older people 66–7
  pregnancy 56–7
  teenagers 64–5
  toddlers and young children 60–3
alcohol 52–3, 56, 147
alkalis in cooking 126
allergies 74–7, 152
amino acids 28, 72
anaphylactic shock 74, 75
anorexia nervosa 65
antioxidants 4, 5, 43, 104
anus 26, 27
AOAC method 41
appearance of food 178
ascorbic acid 42
assessment
  controlled 184–5
  cooking skills 179
  food checks 178
  information technology, use of for 192–3
  planning 188–9
  research 186–7, 190
  sensory analysis 180–1
  task analysis 190–1
avocados 5

B

babies
  diet for 58–9
  ready-prepared baby food 62–3
bacillus cereus 141
bacteria 132, 133, 138–41
baked beans 96
bakeries 103
balance, energy 14, 15
balanced diet 2–3
bananas 5
bar codes 152
basal metabolic rate (BMR) 16
beans 5, 96–7

best before dates 150, 152
binding 114
binge drinking 52, 53
biodegradable packaging 155
biodigesters 167
biofuels 175
bioyoghurt 90, 91
biscuits 125
body fat 18
body mass index (BMI) 18–19
bottling 148
bowel problems 23
bread 36, 102–3, 123
bread-making machines 128–9
breakfast cereals 100
breastfeeding 58
broccoli 5
browning 117
Buddhists and food choices 81
bulking 114, 118
butter 120, 121

C

calcium 46–7
  for elderly people 67
  in fish 87
  during pregnancy 57
  in school meals 78
  for teenagers 64, 65
  for vegetarians 71, 72–3
campylobacter 140
cancer 23
canning 146, 149
carbohydrates 34–5
  or elderly people 67
  pulses and beans 97
  in school meals 79
  for sport and exercise 68
  for teenagers 65
  for toddlers and young children 60
carbon dioxide 122
carbon footprint of food products 165
carotene 44
carrots 5
cereals 100–1, 115
chana dahl 96
Change4Life campaign 15, 19, 38–9
cheese 90–1
chicken 84
chickpeas 96, 97
children 60–3
chilling 146

cholecalciferol 45
cholesterol 31
Christians and food choices 80
chutney 148
Citizens Advice Bureau (CAB) 173
clostridium prefringens 141
cobalamin 42
coeliac disease 76
colour in food 114, 178
colourings 75, 105
combination/composite food 8–9
complementation of protein 29
complex carbohydrates 36
conduction 108
constipation 23
consumer protection 172–3
consumers 160
Consumers' Association 173
controlled assessment 184–5
convection 108
convenience food 106–7
cook-chill food 106–7
cookers 109
cooking
  beans and pulses 96
  bread 103
  changes during 124–5
  eggs in 88
  equipment for 128–9
  food checks 178
  from frozen 145
  fruit and vegetables 94–5, 95
  methods 108–11
  potatoes 98–9
  raising agents 122–3
  reducing costs 171
  safety 137
  skills 178, 179
  temperature 134–5
  trends 162
  see also properties of ingredients
cool bags 145
coronary heart disease (CHD) 22, 32
cost of food 170–1
cross-contamination 138–9
cryogenic freezing 148
cyancobalamin 42

D

danger zone 134
date codes 150, 152
dehydration 52
diabetes 22–3

diet
  adults 66–7
  babies 58–9
  guidelines for 2–3
  older people 66–7
  and pregnancy 56–7
  for sport and exercise 68–9
  toddlers and young children 60–3
  vegetarian 70–3
dietary reference values (DRVs) 10–13
digestion 26–7
diverticular disease 23
DNA food fraud detection 175
drying 146, 149
duodenum 26

E
e-numbers 104
eatwell plate 6–9
egg allergy 75, 89
eggs 88–9
  effect during cooking 125
  properties of 115
8 tips for eating well 3
elderly people 66–7
emulsification 26, 27, 105, 114
energy from food 14–17
  chicken 85
  fish 87
  pulses and beans 97
  school meals 78–9
Englyst method 41
Environmental Health Officers (EHOs) 173
enzymes 26, 27, 132, 133
equipment for cooking 128–9
escheria coli (e. coli) 140
essential amino acids 28, 72
essential fatty acids 31, 87
estimated average requirements (EARs) 10, 12
ethical shopping 164–5
exercise 68–9
Expenditure and Food Survey 162

F
fair testing 182–3
Fairtrade 164–5
fan-assisted ovens 109
farmers' markets 164
farming 174
fat-soluble vitamins 44–5
fat(s) 30–3
  changes during cooking 124, 125
  in chicken 85
  cooking with 110
  effect of heating on 112
  and energy 14
  in fish 87
  in meat 84
  properties and functions of 115, 120–1
  in school meals 78

types of 120
use of by body 27
females
  breastfeeding 58
  estimated average requirements (EARs) 12
  reference nutrient intake (RNI) 13
fibre 40–1
  effect of heating on 112
  during pregnancy 57
  pulses and beans 97
  in school meals 78
  in starchy food 36–7
  use in the body 27
fingerprick test 75
fish 86–7
fish allergy 75
5 A DAY campaign 4–5
flavour in food 114
flavourings 105
flour
  in bread 102
  from cereals 101
  changes during cooking 124, 125
  gelatinisation 116–17
  properties of 115
  types 101
fluoride 49
folate 42
  need for 43
  during pregnancy 57
  in school meals 78
folic acid supplements 56
food
  effect of heat on 112–13
  fortification of 49
  future problems 175
  nutritionally dense 66
  spoilage 132–5
  for sport and exercise 68–9
  symbols 85
food groups 6–9
Food Intolerance Data Bank 75
food intolerances 74–7
food labels 41
  5 A DAY campaign 5
  ethical 168–9
  guideline daily amounts (GDAs) 11
  information on 150–3
  salt 50–1
food miles 165
food poisoning 57, 138–41
food probes 134, 135
Food Standards Agency 3, 6
food symbols 73
formula milk 59
fortification of food 49
fraud detection 175
Freedom Food 85
freezers 144–5
freezing 146, 149
fruit 94–5

5 A DAY campaign 4–5
  properties of 115
frying 121
functional foods 93
functions of ingredients 114–15
  fats 120–1
  flour 116–17
  sugar 116–17

G
gadgets 128
gelatinisation 116–17
genetically modified (GM) food 167
glazing 114
glucose 34
gluten in flour 116–17
gluten intolerance 75, 76
glycaemic index (GI) 35
glycogen 16, 68
guideline daily amounts (GDAs) 11, 153

H
haemorrhoids 23
halal food 80, 81
health
  diet for 2–3
  and obesity 18
  risks linked to poor diet 22–5
heart disease 22, 32
hidden fat 32
hidden sugar 38
high-risk foods 132, 133
Hindus and food choices 80
homogenisation 90
household trends 162
hygiene, personal 136

I
ileum 26
immersion freezing 148
information and communications technology (ICT) 192–3
ingredients
  listed on labels 150
  properties and functions of 114–15
insoluble fibre 40
intestines 26, 27
intolerances, food 74–7
iodine 71, 73
iron
  for elderly people 67
  in fish 87
  lack of 24
  need for 47
  during pregnancy 57
  RNI values 13
  in school meals 78
  sources of 47
  for teenagers 64, 65
  for toddlers and young children 60

for vegetarians 71, 72
irradiation 149

J
jamming 148
Jews and food choices 80

K
kilocalories (kcal) 14
kilojoules (kJ) 14
kosher food 80, 81

L
labour-saving machinery 128–9
lactation 49
lacto ovo vegetarians 70
lacto vegetarians 70
lard 120, 121
large intestines 26, 27
law 172
legislation 172
legumes 96, 97
lentils 96, 97
Lion quality mark 89
listeria 57, 140
liver 26
lower reference nutrient intakes
    (LRNIs) 10

M
macronutrients
    carbohydrates 34–5
    effect of heat on 112
    fats 30–3
    protein 28–9
    starches 36–7
magnesium 48
maize 101
males
    estimated average requirements
        (EARs) 12
    reference nutrient intake (RNI)
        13
margarine 120, 121, 124, 125
marketing 161
Meals on Wheels 67
measurement of energy 14,
    16–17
measurement of fibre 41
meat 84
    substitutes for 92–3
metabolism 66
micronutrients 28
    effect of heat on 113
    minerals 46–9
    vitamins 42–5
microwave cooking 110–11
milk 90
    properties of 115
milk intolerance 75
minerals 27, 46–9, 60, 86, 113
Mobius loop 157
modified atmosphere packaging
    (MAP) 147, 154

modified starch 175
monosaccharides 26
monosodium glutamate 105
moulds 132, 133
mouths 26, 27
Muslims and food choices 80
mycoprotein 92–3

N
nanotechnology 174–5
neural tube defects 56, 57
niacin 42
non-milk extrinsic sugars (NMEs)
    35, 38, 78, 79
non-starch polysaccharides (NSP)
    40
novel foods 93
nutrient requirements 10–11, 12–13
    adults 66
    elderly people 66–7
    protein 28
    teenagers 64–5
    vegetarians 71–3
    young children 60
nutrients
    absorption of 27
    carbohydrates 34–5
    fats 30–3
    minerals 46–9
    protein 28–9
    starches 36–7
    vitamins 42–5
nutritional standards 78
nutritional value
    beans and pulses 96
    cereals 100–1
    cheese 90–1
    chicken 84
    eggs 89
    fish and seafood 86–7
    fruit and vegetables 4–5, 94–5
    meat 84
    milk 90
    potatoes 98
nutritionally dense food 66
nuts 97

O
oats 101
obesity
    health problems from 18
    levels of 18
    losing weight 19–20
    measurement of 18–19
    overeating, reasons for 19–20
oesophagus 26, 27
Ofcom (Office of Communications)
    160
Office of Fair Trading 173
oil 115, 120, 121
older people 66–7
omega 3 and 6 fatty acids 31, 86, 87
oranges 5
organic food 166–7

osteomalacia 25
osteoporosis 47, 66
ovens 109
overeating, reasons for 20–1
overweight, being *see* obesity

P
packaging 154–7, 174
pancreas 26
pasta 36, 101
pasteurisation 148
pasteurised milk 90
pastry, shortcrust 124
pathogenic bacteria 138
peanut allergy 75
peas 96, 97
pester power 160
pesticides 174
pH scale 126
phosphorus 47
physical activity level
    (PAL) 16–17
pickling 148
piles 23
planning 188–9
polylactic acid (PLA) 155
poor diet, risks linked to 22–5
portions, size of 4–5, 20
potassium 48
potatoes 36, 98–9
poultry 85
pregnancy and diet 56–7
preservatives 75, 104
preserving 114, 146–9
price of food 170–1
primary research 186
production of food 166–7
properties of ingredients 114–15
    fats 120–1
    flour 116–17
    sugar 116–17
protein 28–9
    effect of heating on 112
    for elderly people 67
    in fish 86, 87
    during pregnancy 57
    pulses and beans 97
    RNI values 13
    in school meals 78
    soya 92–3
    for sport and exercise 69
    for teenagers 64, 65
    for toddlers and young children
        60
    use of by body 27
    for vegetarians 71, 72
pulses 36, 96–7, 115
pyridoxine 42

Q
Quantitative Ingredient Declaration
    (QUID) 152
questionnaires 186
Quorn™ 92–3

R

radiation 108–9
raising agents 122–3
Rastafarians and food choices 81
ready meals 106
ready-prepared baby food 62–3
recipes
    biscuits 125
    shortcrust pastry 124
    white sauce 124
recycling of packaging 156–7
Red Tractor 85
reduced-fat spreads 120, 121
reference nutrient intakes (RNIs)
    10, 12–13
refrigerators 85, 144
religion and food choices 80–1
research 186–7
retinol 44, 45
riboflavin 42
rice 36, 101
rickets 25
rye 101

S

safety, food
    eggs 89
    hygiene 136
    meat and poultry 85
    nanotechnology 174–5
    preparation of food 137
    shopping 136
    storage 137
saliva 26
salt 50–1, 79, 147
saturated fats 30, 78, 87, 121
sauce, white 124
school meals 78–9
scurvy 25
seafood 86–7
secondary research 186
seeds 97
selenium 49, 71, 73
semi-skimmed milk 90
sensory analysis 180–1
setting food 114
shellfish allergy 75
shopping for food 136, 145, 163–5
shortcrust pastry 124
shortening 114, 120
Sikhs and food choices 81
skimmed milk 90
small intestines 27
smell of food 178
smoking 147
sodium 50, 78
soluble fibre 40
sound of food 178
soya allergy 75
soya beans 97
soya protein 92–3
spina bifida 56, 57
spoilage of food 132–5
sport 68–9

stabilisers 105
standards, nutritional 78
staphylococcus aureus 140, 141
starches 36–7
    effect of heating on 112
    for elderly people 67
    gelatinisation 116–17
    during pregnancy 57
    for teenagers 65
        RNI values 13
    for toddlers and young children
        60
    as type of carbohydrate 34
steam as raising agent 122
stomachs 26, 27
storage 137
    freezers 144–5
    fruit and vegetables 95
    meat and poultry 85
    refrigerators 145
suet 120, 121
sugar 38–9
    effect during cooking 125
    effect of heating on 112
    as preservative 147
    properties and functions 118–19
    properties of 115
    and tooth decay 24
    as type of carbohydrate 34, 35
supplements 56, 68, 69
survey on cooking and shopping
    162
sustainability 166–7
sweeteners 105, 114
symbols
    cooking 109
    food 73
    recycling 157

T

taste of food 178, 180–3
teenagers 64–5
temperature control 134–5, 178
texture of food 114, 178
textured vegetable protein
    (TVP) 92
thiamin 42
    for elderly people 67
    RNI values 13
    for teenagers 64, 65
    for toddlers and young children
        60
thickening 114
time control 134
tocopherol 45
toddlers 60–3
tofu 92
tomatoes 5
tooth decay 24, 38, 63
Trading Standards Officers 172–3
traffic light system 153
trans fats 31
trends in cooking and shopping 162
TV dinners 106

U

UHT (ultra heat treatment) 149
unhealthy diet 2, 22–5
unsaturated fats 30
use by dates 150, 152

V

vacuum packing 147
vegans 70
vegetables 4–5, 94–5
vegetarian diet 70–3, 121
vinegar 147
vitamins 27, 42–5
    A 44, 45, 56, 64, 78, 86, 87
    B 42
    B1 42
    B2 42
    B3 42
    B6 42
    B12 42, 71, 73
    C 13, 25, 42, 57, 64, 65, 67, 71, 72,
        78, 94
    D 25, 44, 45, 46, 57, 60, 65, 67,
        71, 86, 87
    effect of heating on 113
    fat-soluble 44–5
    in fruit and vegetables 95
    K 45
    RNI values 13
    water-soluble 42–3

W

waste, food 167
water
    cooking with 110
    effect during cooking 125
    functions of 52
water-soluble vitamins 42–3
weaning babies 59
weight, body
    health and being overweight 18
    losing 19–21
    obesity levels 18
wheat 101, 102
white sauce 124
women
    breastfeeding 58
    estimated average requirements
        (EARs) 12
    reference nutrient intake (RNI)
        13

Y

yeast 102, 122–3, 132, 133
yoghurt 91

Z

zinc
    in fish 87
    need for 48
    RNI values 13
    in school meals 78
    for teenagers 64, 65